JEWISH
CALENDAR MYSTERY
DISPELLED

Jewish

Calendar Mystery

Dispelled

A SYSTEMATIC STUDY OF THE JEWISH
AND THE GENERAL CALENDAR SYSTEMS

By

GEORGE ZINBERG

VANTAGE PRESS
NEW YORK   WASHINGTON   HOLLYWOOD

Dedicated to the cherished memory
of my parents and to my dear wife
and sons whose encouragement sus-
tained my efforts.

Acknowledgments

I Wish to express my deep appreciation of the elucidating articles on the Jewish calendar found in the Jewish Encyclopedia, The Universal Jewish Encyclopedia, The Encyclopedia Britannica, and The Encyclopedia of Religion and Ethics, all of which immensely contributed to the formulation of my thoughts on this subject.

Preface

THE calendar systems of the various parts of the globe differ substantially from each other. In this work, our attention is focused upon only two of such systems, namely: the Gregorian Calendar, used in the United States and in many other countries, referred to herein as the "General Calendar," and the "Jewish Calendar." These two systems are analyzed, distinguished from, and correlated with, each other. "General," used with date, day, month, or year, denotes the time units of the General Calendar. "Jewish," used with date, day, month, or year, denotes the time units of the Jewish Calendar. This study is confined to a purely scientific point of view. It is not intended to prescribe the portions of the Torah or the Aftora to be read on each Saturday or holiday. Such matters are within the province of religion.

The Jewish calendar system is the heritage of Jewish wisdom and culture of many centuries ago. It has a luni-solar basis. Its intricate technique is stimulating and fascinating. Up to the middle of the 4th century, the Sanhedrin, the elders of Judea, who then had the exclusive authority to set the day of every Jewish holiday, kept the Jewish Calendar Rules a closely guarded secret in order to maintain the dependence of all the scattered Jewish communities upon Jerusalem. These Rules were subsequently published by Patriarch Hillel II in the year 359 A.D., sixteen centuries ago. They still govern all the Jewish calendar calculations.

While necessarily using the calendar systems of their adopted countries, Jewish communities scattered all over the globe, nonetheless, celebrate and observe their holidays, birthdays, wedding anniversaries, and honor the memorial days of their dear ones in accordance with the Jewish calendar. With the rebirth of Israel, the most recent national event which kindled the imagination of every Jew, the Jewish calendar became its official calendar. Independence Day will always be celebrated and remembered as having occurred on the 5th day of Iyar, in the year 5708. The birthdays and memorial days of the famous Jewish leaders who devoted their lives to the Independence idea, and of the national heroes who lost their lives fighting for it, will always be remembered and honored on Jewish dates. All Jewish traditions are inseparably connected with Jewish dates. Widespread knowledge and understanding of the Jewish Calendar System would be a fitting acknowledgment of its national functions and usefulness.

It is, therefore, all the more amazing to find a general lack of knowledge or understanding of the fundamental principles and calculation-methods of the Jewish calendar even among those who are well versed in Jewish literature, religion, history, etc. Very few know even such simple things as the number of days of the Jewish months or years or the frequency and determination of the Jewish Leap Year.

Such lack of understanding must be attributed to the failure of the Jewish schools, yeshivas or colleges to provide a systematic study of the principles and calculation-methods of the Jewish-General Correlated calendar system. The largest and most influential Jewish community in the United States has not produced a single book providing such study for schools or making such knowledge available for self-study. With its secrecy lifted sixteen centuries ago, the Jewish calendar still remains shrouded in mystery.

The object of this work is to dispel the mystery of the Jewish calendar, to formulate its principles and calculation-methods in simple terms, to devise special methods solving all its intricacies, to show the relationship between the Jewish and the General calendars, to show the workings and the peculiar characteristics of each calendar and to devise a Jewish-General correlated calendar system. Instead of having just a vague idea about the Jewish calendar, one may acquire a complete understanding of it and have both calendars function at his home.

Contents

III. CALCULATION METHODS

PART THREE
PERPETUAL GENERAL CALENDAR 1600 TO INFINITY

Part One

Calendar Study

General View of Calendar Study

With the expounding of the principles of the two calendar systems, it is soon discovered that the compiling of a Jewish-General correlated calendar of any Jewish year requires the prior determination of its Three Characteristics, namely:

1. Its NYD—New Year's Day.
2. Its TYPE—showing the number of months in the year, the number of days in each month, and whether the corresponding General year is an Ordinary year (OY) or a Leap year (LY).
3. Its GD—General date of its Tishri 1.

The NYD determination, in turn, requires the prior computation of the New Moon of its Tishri. The following four different calculation-methods are therefore given in regular order, namely: New Moon Computation, NYD Determination, Type Determination, and GD Determination. Two alternative methods are given for the GD Determination. The second, named the Prognosticator Method, was specially devised to determine the GD of any Jewish year on the basis of the GD of a distant prior Jewish year without first determining successively the GD's of all the preceding Jewish years. Every method is fully described and amply demonstrated. These methods have been actually used and applied to determine the Three Characteristics of every one of the 500 Jewish years from 5460 to 5960 listed in

Table 1, which is part of the 500-Year Jewish-General Correlated Calendar given in Part Two.

The purpose of each of these Three characteristics is quite obvious. The NYD is the basis of finding the day of any Jewish date during the year. The TYPE shows the number of months in the year, the number of days in each month, and the Type of the corresponding General year. The GD establishes the link between the Jewish year and its corresponding General year and is used as a basis for finding the General date corresponding to any given Jewish date, and the Jewish date corresponding to any given General date, during the year.

The following specially devised Tables are then described and amply demonstrated:

Table 2A, designed to find the General date corresponding to any given Jewish date.

Table 2B, designed to find the Jewish date corresponding to any given General date.

Table 3, designed to find the day of any given Jewish date.

These Tables enable us to compile the annual Jewish-General Correlated calendar of any one of the 500 Jewish years whose Three Characteristics are given in Table 1. Furthermore, they can be applied to any Jewish year, far beyond the last year listed in Table 1, provided its Three Characteristics have first been determined.

Special attention is invited to Section VII—"A GLANCE AT THE JEWISH YEAR 6000." This is a year far beyond the last year listed in Table 1. The New Moon of its Tishri is computed on the basis of the First New Moon of 5723 years ago.

Its NYD is then determined by the application of the Jewish Calendar Rules. Its TYPE is determined on the basis of this NYD and the NYD of the following year, 6001. Its GD is determined by the Prognosticator Method on the basis of the GD of the Jewish year 5468, which is 532 years prior to the year 6000. Its annual Jewish-General Correlated Calendar, compiled by the application of Tables 2A and 3, shows the date and day of evey Jewish holiday, Independence Day, and other national events. It is a forecast of the annual calendar of the Jewish year 6000 and it demonstrates the use and applicability of the specially devised Methods and Tables in compiling annual calendars of distant future Jewish years.

I.

General Principles

1

Time Units

TIME, like space, is infinite. Only a definite interval of time can be measured. Short intervals of time (less than a day) are measured by the watch or clock. Longer intervals are measured by means of the calendar. Continuing the space analogy, the calendar maps out the time interval. It places signposts along its paths and crossroads, showing distance and direction, and spotlights the points of interest. It establishes a starting point. It provides standards for the measurement of time and its subdivisions. It furnishes a framework into which all events, occurrences, and human activities can be set in their order of succession, which is essential for a proper evaluation and appraisal of their historical significance. The calendar is also used as a guide in the regulation of human activities.

STARTING POINT

The General calendar adopted the birth of Christ as the beginning of its era. The year, together with the initials "A.D." or "B.C." designate respectively the number of years after or before the beginning of the General era. Like many other nations, the Jews of ancient times reckoned their years from the happenings of important events, such as the Exodus, or some easily remembered occurrence, such as the beginning of the reign of a king. The era now in universal use among Jews of modern times was adopted in the third century A.D. It is said to begin with Creation, which was then calculated to have taken place in the fall of the year 3761 B.C. The beginning of the Jewish calendar era thus antedates the beginning of the General Calendar era by 3761 years, despite the fact that the Jewish Calendar era was not adopted until the third century after the beginning of the General Calendar era. The Jewish year, which is now counted from the beginning of the Jewish Calendar era, is therefore numerically greater by 3761 than its corresponding General year.

The Jewish year is generally shown with the thousands omitted. The Jewish year 5714, for instance, is shown as 714, which is 5000 less than the full Jewish year. With the omission of 5000 the Jewish year is smaller than its corresponding General year by 1239. The General year corresponding to a given Jewish year is therefore found by adding 1239 to the given Jewish year, and the Jewish year corresponding to a given General year is the General year minus 1239. For that part of the Jewish year which continues after January 1, when the General year increases by 1, the difference becomes 1240 instead of 1239.

STANDARDS OF MEASUREMENT

Observations in the early days revealed that the following natural phenomena occur and recur with constant regularity: 1) the rotation of the earth about its axis, 2) the appearance of the moon in all its phases from New Moon to New Moon, and 3) the revolution of the earth in its orbit around the sun. The periods of time in which these phenomena occur are known respectively as: the day, the lunar month, and the solar year. These are natural time units determined by natural phenomena. The second, the minute, the hour, the week, the calendar month, and the calendar year are conventional time units fixed and adopted for convenience.

THE DAY

The smallest natural time unit, the Day, has been adopted as the basic time unit. Day is used here in the sense of comprising darkness and light, night and day. It is divided into 24 Hours. The Hour is divided into 60 Minutes. The Minute is divided into 60 Seconds. The Second is the equivalent of the semi-oscillation of the pendulum of a clock. The Jewish calendar also recognizes the subdivision of the Hour into 1080 Parts. There are 18 such Parts in a Minute. Each Part is equal to $3\frac{1}{3}$ Seconds.

For computation purposes, time will be shown under the initials *D H M S* designating Days, Hours, Minutes, and Seconds. Parts, rather than Seconds, are used in the New Moon computations. Time is there shown under the initials *D H M P*.

Beginning of the Day

The General day begins at midnight, and ends the following midnight. The Jewish day begins 6 hours earlier, at 6 P.M., and ends the following 6 P.M. This is in accordance with the biblical account of creation: "And there was evening and there was morning, one day." The beginning of the Jewish day should not be confused with the beginnings of the Sabbath, holidays, or fast days. For religious purposes, these are set to begin at sunset and to end with the appearance of the stars on the following evening, or, if the holiday has two days, on the subsequent evening.

Variations of the Time of the Day

Although the time of the day is a fixed period of 24 hours, it is not so for those who travel from east to west or from west to east. A person completing a journey from New York to California in one day finds that his day is lengthened by 3 hours. The clocks in California are set 3 hours earlier. The traveler from New York to Belgium completing his journey by plane in one day finds that his day is shortened by 6 hours. The Belgian clocks are set 6 hours later. One completing a journey around the globe finds a difference in a whole day of 24 hours.

This is due to the fact that as the earth rotates about its axis its 360 meridians follow one another in meeting the sun at sunrise and leaving it at sunset. Since it takes 24 hours for all the 360 meridians to meet the sun at sunrise, only 15 meridians do so each hour. Sunrise, sunset, and consequently midnight are therefore one hour apart for places 15 degrees (or meridians) apart from each other. Thus the continental United States is divided into four time-belts 15 degress apart: The Eastern, Central, Mountain, and

Pacific. Greenwich time, which is that of the meridian at 0°, is considered the base. Eastern Standard Time is 5 hours earlier. The time of each succeeding belt is one hour earlier than that of its preceding belt. Eastern Standard Time is that of the meridian at 75°. Pacific Time is that of the meridian at 120°. The meridian at 180°, directly back of the Greenwich Time meridian, has been adopted as the International Date Line. Here, there is a difference of a whole day of 24 hours between both sides of the meridian. A person traveling from the United States to Japan, via the Pacific Ocean, sets his time a day forward on crossing the International Date Line. The traveler from Japan to the United States, via the Pacific Ocean, sets his time back one day at that line.

Ordinarily, such loss or gain of a full day may cause no more than momentary excitement. If, however, the traveler is a religious observer of the Sabbath and on his way from the United States to Japan, via the Pacific Ocean, reaches the International Date Line on Friday just before sunset and must set his time one full day ahead, what happens to his Sabbath? If, on the other hand, he is on his way from Japan to the United States, via the Pacific Ocean, and he reaches the International Date Line on Saturday evening and he must set his time back one full day, must he observe a second Sabbath? Some Rabbi may some day give us the answer.

The Lunar Month

The period during which the moon appears in all its phases of illumination (new moon, waxing moon, full moon and waning moon) from New Moon to New Moon, is known as the lunar month. The New Moon occurs regularly every 29 days, 12 hours, 44 minutes, and 3⅓ seconds (1

Part). The Jewish calendar month is based on the lunar month. The General calendar month has no relation whatsoever to the lunar month.

THE SOLAR YEAR

THE SEASONS. The earth makes a complete revolution in its orbit around the sun every 365 days, 5 hours, 48 minutes, and 46 seconds. This period is known as the solar year. As the earth revolves around the sun and rotates about its axis, the heat received by the various parts of its spherical surface varies during the year. The length of night and the length of day likewise vary during the year. By reason of such variations, the year is divided into four seasons, namely: spring, summer, autumn, and winter. The beginnings of these seasons in the northern hemisphere correspond respectively to the four positions of the earth at points dividing the orbit into four quarters. The two positions corresponding to the beginnings of spring and autumn are called equinoxes, i.e., the point at which the lengths of night and day are equal. The spring equinox is also known as the vernal equinox. The two positions corresponding to the beginnings of summer and winter are called solstices. At these points the sun is furthest from the equator and stops receding further. The General dates of the beginnings of the four seasons have been fixed as follows: spring —March 21, summer—June 21, autumn—September 23, and winter—December 22. In the southern hemisphere, the seasons are just the opposite of those in the northern hemisphere. Thus when it is summer in the northern hemisphere, it is winter in the southern hemisphere.

2

The General Calendar

THE General year is based on the solar year. The calendar year, however, must have a whole number of days without fractions so that it may always begin at the beginning of the day, at midnight. The General Ordinary year therefore has only 365 days and is consequently less than the solar year by 5 hours, 48 minutes, and 46 seconds. In four years these annual differences accumulate to 23 hours, 15 minutes, and 4 seconds. To adjust such differences, the Julian Calendar, adopted by Julius Caesar in the year 46 B.C., provided that every fourth year, the year divisible by 4, should be a Leap year having 366 days. The additional day is added to the month of February.

THE GREGORIAN REFORMATION

The additional full day exceeded the accumulated four-year difference by 44 minutes and 56 seconds. In 400 years, such excess accumulated to 74 hours, 53 minutes, and 20 seconds. The Julian Calendar was therefore reformed by Pope Gregory XIII in the year 1582 A.D., as follows:

a) Ten days were suppressed by counting October 5th as October 15th.

b) It was ordered that three out of every four century years, beginning with the year 1700, those whose hundreds are not divisible by 4, shall be Ordinary years.

The rule for determining Leap years may therefore be stated as follows:

"Every year divisible by four, *except century years of which the hundreds are not divisible by four*, is a Leap year."

Thus reformed, the calendar became known as the Gregorian Calendar.

Further Adjustment Proposed

It must be noted that the excess accumulated over every 400-year period is 74 hours, 53 minutes, and 20 seconds. The provision that three out of every four century years shall not be Leap years, eliminated only 3 days (72 hours) of such excess thus leaving an unadjusted excess of 2 hours, 53 minutes and 20 seconds. Over a 3323-year period, such unadjusted excess will accumulate to a whole day. It was therefore proposed to adjust such unadjusted excess by making the year 4000 and multiples thereof Ordinary years. The reason for proposing the year 4000 and its multiples instead of the year 3323 is to continue the number 4 in the adjustment period. The remaining unadjusted excess would then be so small as to amount to less than one day in 200 centuries. This, however, is still only a proposal.

The General Month

A division of the solar year by the lunar month shows 12 lunar months plus a remainder of 10 days 21 hours and 6 seconds, as shown by the following figures.

	D	H	M	S
One lunar month	29	12	44	$3\frac{1}{3}$
Multiply by 12			x12	
	354	08	48	40
One solar year	365	05	48	46
Twelve lunar months	354	08	48	40
Remainder	10	21	00	06

The number of lunar months in the solar year originated the idea of having 12 months in a year. The large remainder, however, rendered the lunar month inadaptable as a subdivision of the General year. The General year was therefore arbitrarily divided into twelve General months, having no relation whatsoever to the lunar month, with respective numbers of days as follows:

January	31	April	30	July	31	October	31
February	28*	May	31	August	31	November	30
March	31	June	30	September	30	December	31

* February has 29 days in a Leap Year.

II.

Fundamentals of the Jewish Calendar

3

The Jewish Calendar Has a Luni-Solar Basis

THE Jewish era, the Jewish day and its subdivisions, and their relationship to the General era, the General day and its subdivisions, were discussed in the preceding chapter. We will now discuss the other time units of the Jewish Calendar, namely: the month and the year. Some Jewish holidays are closely interwoven with both the lunar month and the solar year. Passover, for instance, is set to begin on the eve of the 15th day (full moon) of Nissan, but must not occur before the beginning of spring, a subdivision of the solar year. Nissan is known as "Chodesh Aviv," the month of spring. Succoth, the Feast of Tabernacles, known as "Hag-Ha-Asif,"—the holiday of the gathering of the crops, is set to begin on the eve of the 15th day (full moon) of Tishri and is also identified with autumn, the end of the harvesting season. In their steadfast adherence to tradition, the Jews have clung to the lunar month as a basis of the Jewish month, despite its inadaptability as a subdivision of the solar year. In order, however, to maintain the necessary relationship between the Jewish holidays and the seasons, which are subdivisions of the solar year, the Jewish calendar adopted the solar year as a basis of the Jewish year. The Jewish calendar is thus based on both the lunar month and the solar year. It has a Luni-Solar basis.

4

The Jewish Month

THE lunar month, as we have seen, has 29 days, 12 hours, 44 minutes, and 3⅓ seconds. Its fractional part of the day causes the New Moons to occur and the lunar months to begin at all times of the day. The calendar month, however, must always begin at the beginning of the day and must have a whole number of days without fractions. Since the fractional part of the day contained in the lunar month is approximately half a day (12 hours, 44 minutes, and 3⅓ seconds), the Jewish months were made to alternate between 30 and 29 days. Further adjustments were made by varying some of the Jewish months between 29 and 30 days for different Types of the Jewish year as will be shown later.

THE BEGINNING OF THE JEWISH MONTH. ROSH CHODESH.

"Rosh Chodesh" is a Hebrew expression denoting the first day of the month. There is obviously only one day in the month which can bear that name. Nevertheless, some Jewish months have two days Rosh Chodesh and others only one. Furthermore, some Jewish months have two days

Rosh Chodesh in certain Types of the Jewish year and only one day in other Types of the Jewish year. The natural tendency is to consider the first day Rosh Chodesh as the first day of the month and the second day Rosh Chodesh as the second day of the month. There is nothing further from the truth. The so-called "first day Rosh Chodesh" is neither the first day nor any day of the month of which it is designated as Rosh Chodesh. The confusion is due to the fact that the last day of every 30-day month was named and observed as the First Day Rosh Chodesh of the following month. The first day of the following month, the actual Rosh Chodesh, was then named the Second Day Rosh Chodesh. Thus every Jewish month following a 30-day month has two days Rosh Chodesh and every Jewish month following a 29-day month has only one day, its first day, correctly named Rosh Chodesh. The confusing designation of the last day of the 30-day month as the first day Rosh Chodesh of the following 29-day month is the direct cause of the prevailing erroneous presumption that the 30-day month has only 29 days and that the 29-day month has 30 days. Small wonder that many Jews do not know how many days there are in any particular month. As a basic unit of the Jewish calendar, the Jewish month should be clearly understood and its beginning and ending should never be confused. The Table of Jewish months for every Type of year, given later in this work, is designed to eliminate confusion.

5

The Jewish Year

THE NORMAL JEWISH ORDINARY YEAR

THE calendar year must have a whole number of months, without fractions, so that it may always begin at the beginning of the month. Using the lunar month as a basis for the Jewish month, the Jewish calendar set up a year of twelve months alternating between 29 and 30 days and aggregating 354 days as a near approximation of twelve lunar months. This Type of Jewish year is known as the Normal Ordinary year.

SEVEN JEWISH LEAP YEARS IN EVERY NINETEEN-YEAR CYCLE

Twelve lunar months are far less than the solar year as shown by the following figures:

	D	H	M	S
One solar year	365	5	48	46
12 lunar months	354	8	48	40
Annual difference	10	21	00	06

This annual difference, carried from year to year, would

cause each Jewish year to begin almost 11 days earlier in the solar year than its predecessor. Passover, a spring holiday, would soon recede from spring into winter and into autumn, etc. To adjust such differences and to raise the Jewish year to a nearer approximation of the solar year, it was obviously necessary to add a whole (thirteenth) month to some Jewish years. The frequency of such additions depended upon finding the number of solar years in which the annual differences accumulate to a whole number of lunar months.

It was found that in nineteen solar years these annual differences very nearly approximated seven lunar months, as shown by the following:

	D	H	M	S
Annual difference	10	21	00	06
Multiply by 19		x19		
19-year difference	206	15	01	15
One lunar month	29	12	44	$3\frac{1}{3}$
Multiply by 7		x7		
7 lunar months	206	17	8	$23\frac{1}{3}$

That nineteen solar years were a very near equivalent of 235 lunar months, was discovered by Meton, an Athenian astronomer (432 B.C.). The nineteen-year period is therefore known as the Metonic cycle. Based on the Metonic cycle, the Jewish calendar adopted a system of having every 19-year period consist of 12 Ordinary (12-month) years and 7 Leap (13-month) years, counted from the beginning of the Jewish era. The 13th month, named V-Adar, having 29 days, is interposed between Adar and Nissan, the sixth and seventh months respectively, in the 3rd, 6th, 8th, 11th, 14th, 17th, and 19th years of every nineteen-year period, which is now known as the nineteen-year cycle. The month of Adar is also increased from 29 to 30 days in every Leap year. The Jewish Leap year therefore has 30 days more than the Jewish Ordinary year.

JEWISH LEAP YEAR DETERMINATION

Divide the given Jewish year, thousands included, by 19. The quotient shows the number of cycles that have elapsed since the beginning of the Jewish era. The remainder shows which year it is in the current cycle. If it is one of those fixed as Leap years, it is a Leap year. Otherwise, it is an Ordinary year. The year 5714, for instance, divided by 19, shows a quotient of 300 and a remainder of 14, indicating that it is the 14th year in the 301st cycle. It is a Leap year.

THE BEGINNING OF THE JEWISH YEAR.

ROSH HASHANA. The first month of the Jewish year is Tishri. The first day of Tishri is the first day of the Jewish year and is known as Rosh Hashana. The day of the week on which Tishri 1 occurs is the Jewish New Year's Day, designated by the abbreviation NYD. The day of the week on which January 1 occurs is the General New Year's Day, likewise designated by the abbreviation NYD. The former is known as the Jewish NYD; the latter is known as the General NYD. The Jewish NYD is determined in accordance with the Jewish Calendar Rules and is based on the New Moon of Tishri, which is derived by computation, as shown in the following chapter.

Many years ago New Moon computation was unknown. The New Moon was then determined by observation from the mountaintops. The appearance of the New Moon was then heralded by messengers to all parts of Judea and to all scattered communities. With traveling and means of communication in their primitive stages, the observation results frequently failed to reach the scattered communities in time to determine the days when holidays were to be celebrated or observed. For fear of failing to celebrate a holiday on its proper day, the scattered communities adopted a general rule of celebrating every Jewish holiday on two consecutive days. Yom Kippur was excepted from this rule. Although the New Moon is now accurately computed and there is no doubt as to the days on which the Jewish holidays are to be observed, all the orthodox Jews in the Diaspora still continue to observe every Jewish holiday, except Yom Kippur, on two consecutive days. Both the first and the second days of Tishri are celebrated and observed as Rosh Hashana. For calendar purposes, however, only Tishri 1 is the Jewish NYD. Its corresponding General date is either in September or early in October.

THE JEWISH NYD CANNOT OCCUR ON WEDNESDAY, FRIDAY, OR SUNDAY

If the Jewish NYD occurred on Wednesday, or Friday, then Yom Kippur (Tishri 10) would fall on Friday or Sunday, immediately preceding or following Saturday. Two such days of complete rest, however, must not immediately precede or follow one another, because that would greatly interfere with the preparation of meals. If the Jewish NYD occurred on Sunday, then Hoshana Rabba (Tishri 21) would fall on Saturday and the physical Hoshana ritual would violate the Sabbath.

The First Day of Passover Cannot Occur on Wednesday, Friday, or Monday

The period that intervenes between the first day of Passover and the first day of Tishri of the following year is invariably 163 days, or 23 weeks and 2 days. If the first day of Passover occurred on Wednesday, Friday, or Monday, then the following Jewish New Year's Day would fall on Friday, Sunday, or Wednesday, respectively, the days on which New Year's Day must not occur. Hence, the first day of Passover cannot occur on Wednesday, Friday, or Monday.

The Jewish NYD is Governed by the Rules

The Rules that guided the Sanhedrin, the governing group of Jewish Elders of Judea, in their computation of the Jewish festivals were kept a jealously guarded secret in order to continue the dependence of the scattered communities upon Judea and thus preserve their ties to the homeland. The days appointed for the Jewish festivals, as computed by the Sanhedrin in accordance with the secret Rules, were communicated to the distant communities by special messengers. In the middle of the 4th century, however, persecutions rendered such communications impossible. Patriarch Hillel II then published the secret Rules to enable the distant communities to make their own computations of the calendar and to determine for themselves the days of the Jewish festivals, without depending upon the Sanhedrin. Fully aware of the fact that the publication of the Rules would sever the last ties that bound the scattered communities to the Partriarchate and thus lessen the dignity of his own House, he performed this deed of self-denial in order to preserve the perpetuity of Judaism. The

Sanhedrin were in full agreement with Patriarch Hillel II. They demanded, however, that the communities outside of Palestine adhere to the customs of their fathers and continue to observe every Jewish holiday on two consecutive days as they did until then, even though the reason therefor disappeared with the publication of the Rules and the elimination of all uncertainty.

6

The Rules of the Jewish Calendar

THE Rules promulgated by Patriarch Hillel II in the middle of the 4th century, A.D., provide as follows:

I The first day of Tishri, the Jewish New Year's Day, is on the day of the New Moon (Molad) of Tishri, except:

a) When such New Moon occurs on Wednesday, Friday, or Sunday, or

b) When such New Moon occurs at noon or later, or

c) When the New Moon of Tishri of an Ordinary year occurs on Tuesday at 11 minutes and 6 parts after 3 A.M. or later, or

d) When, at the termination of a Leap year, such New Moon occurs on Monday at 32 Minutes and 13 parts after 9 A.M. or later.

In each of these events, New Year's Day is shifted from the day of the New Moon of Tishri to the following day or, if the following day is within exception (a), to the subsequent day.

II Every nineteen year cycle, counted from the beginning
of the Jewish era, has seven Leap years, namely: the
3rd, 6th, 8th, 11th, 14th, 17th, and 19th years of the
cycle.

III The New Moon of Tishri of the first year of the Jewish
era, known as the First New Moon, occurred on
(General) Sunday at 11 minutes and 6 parts after
11 P.M.

According to the Jewish reckoning, it occurred on Monday
at 5 hours, 11 minutes, and 6 parts after the beginning of
the day (6 P.M.). General days are used in all New Moon
computations.

Rule I fixes the day of the week of Tishri 1. The Jewish
NYD is based on the New Moon of Tishri. The reasons for
exception (a) have already been shown. Exception (b) is
most probably explained by the fact that the last quarter
of the Jewish day is too close to the end of the day. Exceptions (c) and (d) are closely related to the discussions on
the Type of the Jewish year and will be explained later in
connection with that subject.

Rule II fixes the seven Leap years in every nineteen-year
cycle.

Rule III gives the time when the First New Moon of
Tishri occurred. This is used as a starting point from which
the New Moon of Tishri of any subsequent year is computed.

Six Types of the Jewish Year

The Jewish Ordinary year of 12 months, alternating between 30 and 29 days and having 354 days, is the Normal year, Type N. The shifting of the day of Tishri 1, as prescribed by Rule I, makes it necessary to increase some years and to decrease others by one day. The decrease is effected by reducing Kislev from 30 to 29 days. This is the Deficient year, Type D. The increase is effected by increasing Heshwan from 29 to 30 days. This is the Full year, Type F. The Ordinary year is therefore one of three Types: D, N, or F, and varies from 353 to 355 days. The identical variations occur in the Leap year. Its three Types are DL, NL, or FL, having 383, 384, or 385 days respectively. The letter L is added to the Type of every Leap year to differentiate it from the Ordinary year. The thirteenth month, V-Adar of 29 days is interposed between Adar and Nissan, and Adar is increased from 29 to 30 days, giving every Leap year 30 days more than its corresponding Type of the Ordinary year.

Table of Jewish Months for Every Type of Year

The following Table shows the Jewish months and days for every Type of year. This Table is easily remembered if properly understood. Type N has 12 months alternating between 30 and 29 days, aggregating 354 days. Types D and F have the same months and days, except that Kislev is reduced from 30 to 29 days for Type D, and Heshwan is increased from 29 to 30 days for Type F. Types DL, NL, and FL follow the same pattern, except that the 13th month, V-ADAR, is interposed between Adar and Nissan, and ADAR is increased from 29 to 30 days.

Jewish Months and Respective Days

Month	D	N	F	DL	NL	FL
Tishri	30	30	30	30	30	30
Heshwan	29	29	30	29	29	30
Kislev	29	30	30	29	30	30
Tebet	29	29	29	29	29	29
Shebat	30	30	30	30	30	30
Adar	29	29	29	30	30	30
V-Adar	—	—	—	29	29	29
Nissan	30	30	30	30	30	30
Iyar	29	29	29	29	29	29
Sivan	30	30	30	30	30	30
Tamuz	29	29	29	29	29	29
Ab	30	30	30	30	30	30
Elul	29	29	29	29	29	29
	353	354	355	383	384	385

III.

Calculation Methods

7

Three Elements Needed for the Jewish Annual Calendar

ONLY one element of the General year is needed for the preparation of its annual calendar, namely: the day of January 1, its NYD. The months and their respective days are all alike for every year, except that February is increased from 28 to 29 days in a Leap year. The Leap year occurs with constant regularity in every year divisible by 4, except in century years, of which the hundreds are not divisible by 4. The Jewish year is entirely different. Three elements are needed for the preparation of its annual calendar, namely:

1. The day of its Tishri 1, its NYD.

2. Its Type and the Type of its corresponding General year, its CORRELATED TYPE.

3. The General date corresponding to its Tishri 1, its GD.

8

New Moon Computation

THE Jewish NYD is based on the New Moon of Tishri, which is derived by computation. Our first task is therefore to master New Moon computation.

The time when the New Moon of Tishri occurs is shown by the number of days, hours, minutes, and parts that elapsed since the beginning of the week, at the beginning of Sunday (midnight). The First New Moon, as given by Rule III, for instance, is shown as follows:

D	H	M	P
0	23	11	06

indicating that 0 days, 23 hours, 11 minutes, and 6 parts have elapsed since the beginning of Sunday. It occurred on Sunday, at 11 minutes and 6 parts after 11 P.M.

Any subsequent New Moon is found by adding to the First New Moon figures the days, hours, minutes, and parts that elapsed since then. It must be observed that, in all these computations, 18 parts or multiples are carried to minutes, 60 minutes or multiples are carried to hours, 24 hours or multiples are carried to days and 7 days or multiples are discarded. Zero days indicate Sunday, one day indicates Monday, etc. Single digit figures for hours, minutes, and parts are shown with 0 in front for the sake of uniformity with two-digit figures.

Formulated Expressions of Elapsed Periods

The period that elapsed between the known and its subsequent New Moon may consist of one lunar month, one Ordinary year (12 lunar months), one Leap year (13 lunar months), one cycle (12 Ordinary and 7 Leap years) or any multiple of any one of these units or any combination thereof. To facilitate the New Moon computations, the most commonly occurring elapsed periods have been formulated and expressed as follows:

	D	H	M	P
1 Lunar month	1	12	44	01
1 Ordinary year	4	08	48	12
1 Leap year	5	21	32	13
1 Cycle	2	16	33	01
10 cycles	5	21	30	10
100 cycles	2	23	05	10
300 cycles	1	21	16	12

The lunar month expression is derived from the lunar month period with 4 weeks discarded. The Ordinary year expression was derived by discarding 350 days from its period. 378 days were discarded from the Leap year period. The cycle expression is the combination of the expressions of 12 Ordinary and 7 Leap years with full weeks discarded, etc.

If the lunar month expression is added to the First New Moon, we get the New Moon of Heshwan of the first year of the Jewish era. The addition of the Ordinary year expression to the First New Moon gives the New Moon of Tishri of the second year of the Jewish era. The addition of the cycle expression will show the New Moon of Tishri of the year 20. The 10-cycle expression is added to show the New Moon of Tishri of the year 191, etc. The New Moon of Tishri of 5701 is derived by adding the 300 cycle expression to the First New Moon, as follows:

	D	H	M	F
First New Moon	0	23	11	06
300 cycles	1	21	16	12
Tishri 5701	2	20	28	00

indicating that it occurred on Tuesday at 28 minutes after 8 P.M.

The following computations will demonstrate.

1. The New Moon of Tishri 5720 is computed as follows: 5720 divided by 19 shows that it is the first year in the 302d cycle and that the elapsed period is 301 cycles. Its New Moon of Tishri is therefore found by adding the expressions of 300 cycles and of 1 cycle to the First New Moon, as follows:

	D	H	M	F
First New Moon	0	23	11	06
300 cycles	1	21	16	12
1 cycye	2	16	33	01
Tishri 5720	5	13	01	01

It occurred on Friday at 1 minute and 1 part after 1 P.M.

2. The New Moon of Tishri 5714 is computed as follows:

5714 divided by 19 shows that it is the 14th year in the 301st cycle and that the elapsed period is 300 cycles, 9 Ordinary, and 4 Leap years. Its New Moon of Tishri is found by adding the expressions of 300 cycles, 9 Ordinary years and 4 Leap years to the First New Moon, as follows:

	D	H	M	P
First New Moon	0	23	11	06
300 cycles	1	21	16	12
9 Ordinary years	4	07	18	00
4 Leap years	2	14	10	16
Tishri 5714	2	17	56	16

It occurred on Tuesday at 56 minutes and 16 parts after 5 P.M.

3. Any known New Moon, not necessarily the First New Moon, may be used as a basis for determining a subsequent New Moon. In the following series of years, beginning with the year 5701, only the New Moon of Tishri 5701 was determined on the basis of the First New Moon. It was then used as a basis for determining the New Moon of Tishri of 5702 and each newly determined New Moon of Tishri was used to compute the New Moon of Tishri of the following year by adding successively the Ordinary or Leap year expression in the same order as they follow in the cycle, as follows:

	D	H	M	P
First New Moon	0	23	11	06
300 cycles	1	21	16	12
Tishri 5701	2	20	28	00
1 Ordinary year	4	08	48	12
Tishri 5702	0	05	16	12
1 Ordinary year	4	08	48	12
Tishri 5703*	4	14	05	06
1 Leap year	5	21	32	13
Tishri 5704	3	11	38	01
1 Ordinary year	4	08	48	12
Tishri 5705	0	20	26	13
1 Ordinary year	4	08	48	12
Tishri 5706*	5	05	15	07
1 Leap year	5	21	32	13
Tishri 5707	4	02	48	02
1 Ordinary year	4	08	48	12
Tishri 5708*	1	11	36	14
1 Leap year	5	21	32	13
Tishri 5709	0	09	09	09

* Leap years.

The New Moon computations furnish the basis for the determination of the Jewish NYD and thus constitute a basic factor in the Jewish calendar calculations. It was therefore deemed necessary to dwell upon this subject at length and to demonstrate the various combinations so that New Moon computations be thoroughly understood and done with ease. The time consumed on this basic factor will be found to have been well spent.

9

The Jewish NYD

THE Jewish NYD is based on the New Moon of Tishri and is determined by the application of Rule I, stated as follows:

Tishri 1 is on the day of the New Moon of Tishri, except:

a) When such New Moon occurs on Wednesday, Friday, or Sunday, or

b) When such new Moon occurs at noon or later, or

c) When such New Moon of an Ordinary years occurs on Tuesday at 11 minutes and 6 parts after 3 A.M. or later, or

d) When at the termination of a Leap year, such New Moon occurs on Monday at 32 minutes and 13 parts after 9 A.M. or later,

in which events it is shifted to the following day, or if the following day comes within exception (a), to the subsequent day.

The following illustration shows the NYD determinations of the series of years, beginning with 5714, by the application of Rule I to the New Moons of Tishri. The day of the New Moon of Tishri of each year is shown under NM. The applicable exception, if any, is shown next to it. The NYD is either the same as the NM or it is shifted by reason of the applicable exception.

Year	D	H	M	P	NM	Exceptions	NYD
5714°	2	17	56	16	Tue	(b) and (a)	Thu
	5	21	32	13			
5715	1	15	29	11	Mon	(b)	Tue
	4	08	48	12			
5716	6	00	18	05	Sat	none	Sat
	4	08	48	12			
5717°	3	09	06	17	Wed	(a)	Thu
	5	21	32	13			
5718	2	06	39	12	Tue	(c) and (a)	Thu
	4	08	48	12			
5719°	6	15	28	06	Sat	(b) and (a)	Mon
	5	21	32	13			
5720	5	13	01	01	Fri	(b)	Sat
	4	08	48	12			
5721	2	21	49	13	Tue	(b) and (a)	Thu
	4	08	48	12			
5722°	0	06	38	07	Sun	(a)	Mon
	5	21	32	13			
5723	6	04	11	02	Sat	none	Sat
	4	08	48	12			
5724	3	12	59	14	Wed	(b)	Thu
	4	08	48	12			
5725°	0	21	48	08	Sun	(b)	Mon
	5	21	32	13			
5726	6	19	21	03	Sat	(b) and (a)	Mon

° Leap years

Based on the previously computed New Moon of Tishri 5714, the New Moons of Tishri of the subsequent years of the foregoing series were derived by successive additions of the Ordinary or Leap year expressions in the same order as they follow each other in the cycle. The New Moon of Tishri 5714 is on Tuesday afternoon and is within exception (b), and the following day is within exception (a). Its NYD is therefore shifted to Thursday. The NM of 5718 is within exception (c), and the following day is within exception (a). Its NYD is shifted from Tuesday to Thursday. Exception (d) is very rarely applicable. The NM of 5766, which comes within this exception, illustrates its applicability. The NYD of that year is shifted from Monday to Tuesday.

10

Type of the Jewish Year

Six Types

Each of the two basic Types of the Jewish year, the Ordinary and the Leap year, has three variations: Deficient, Normal, and Full. The Ordinary year variations designated as D, N, and F, have 353, 354, and 355 days respectively. The Leap year variations designated as DL, NL, and FL, have 383, 384, and 385 days respectively. The Ordinary Normal year has twelve months, alternating between 30 and 29 days, with a total of 354 days. Heshwan and Kislev, its second and third months, have 29 and 30 days respectively. Kislev is reduced by one day for the Deficient year and Heshwan is increased by one day for the Full year. The Leap year has the same variations and for each variation it has a thirteenth month, V-Adar—29 days, interposed between Adar and Nissan, and its Adar is increased from 29 to 30 days. Every Leap year variation therefore has 30 days more than its corresponding Ordinary year variation. All the variations of both, the Ordinary and the Leap year, are the six different Types of the Jewish year.

END OF JEWISH YEAR IS ADJUSTED TO THE BEGINNING OF THE FOLLOWING YEAR BY CHOICE OF TYPE

Unlike the General year, which may end on any day of the week, the Jewish year cannot end on Tuesday, Thursday, or Saturday, because the following year cannot begin on Wednesday, Friday, or Sunday. Furthermore, the Jewish NYD is determined on the basis of the New Moon of Tishri, without reference to the ending of the preceding year. The ending of the Jewish year must therefore be adjusted to occur on the day preceding the NYD of the following year. The General conception, that the new year begins when the old year ends, is completely reversed in the case of the Jewish year. The Jewish year ends when the new year begins. The Jewish year is fitted to the previously determined NYD of the following year by choosing that Type of Jewish year which fills the days, exclusive of weeks, between the NYD of the year and the NYD of the following year.

TYPE DETERMINATION

The six different Types of the Jewish year, expressed in days, with full weeks discarded are as follows:

Type	Days	Type	Days
D	3	DL	5
N	4	NL	6
F	5	FL	0

The days, exclusive of weeks, between the NYD of the year and that of the following year are found by expressing each NYD by the number of days that elapsed since the beginning of the week, at the beginning of Sunday, and subtracting the numerical expression of the NYD of the year from that of the following year. If the expression of the NYD of the following year is less than that of the year, first add 7 to the expression of the NYD of the following year and then subtract. This difference, NYD-Difference, determines the Type of the year. If the NYD-difference is 3, the Type of the year is D; if it is 4, the Type is N; if it is 5, the Type is F for an Ordinary year or DL for a Leap year. The difference of 6 shows Type NL and O shows Type FL.

In the following illustration, the series of years beginning with 714, previously used to demonstrate the NYD determinations, is again used to demonstrate the Type determinations. Every NYD's numerical expression is shown next to the NYD. The difference between the expression of the NYD of the year and that of the following year is shown under NYD-DIFF for each year. The NYD-Difference of each year indicates its Type which is shown under Type. The 714 Type is 9-4, namely: DL for a Leap year. The 715 Type is 6-2, Tyne N. The 720 Type is 11-6, Type F for an Ordinary year.

Type Determinations—Illustration

Year	NYD	Num. Express	NYD-Diff	Type
714*	THU	4	5	DL
715	TUE	2	4	N
716	SAT	6	5	F
717*	THU	4	0	FL
718	THU	4	4	N
719*	MON	1	5	DL
720	SAT	6	5	F
721	THU	4	4	N
722*	MON	1	5	DL
723	SAT	6	5	F
724	THU	4	4	N
725*	MON	1	0	FL
726	MON	1		

* Leap years.

Reasons for Exceptions (c) and (d) of Rule I.

We are now in a position to understand the reasons for exceptions (c) and (d) of Rule I.

Exception (c) applies to the New Moon of Tishri of an *Ordinary year* occurring on Tuesday at 11 minutes and 6 parts after 3 A.M. or later. Its NYD must be shifted to Thursday. The reason for this exception will readily appear from the New Moon computation and the NYD and Type determination on the facts stated in the exception.

	D	H	M	P	NYD	Ex-press	NYD Diff	Type
Tishri given year	2	03	11	06	THU	4	4	N
1 Ord. year	4	08	48	12				
Tishri following yr.	6	12	00	00	MON	1		

The New Moon of Tishri of the following year, computed on the basis of the given New Moon, occurs on Saturday at Noon. Its NYD must be shifted to Monday, expressed by 1. The Type of the given year is 8-4, Type N. Without the shifting prescribed by exception (c), the NYD of the given year would be TUE, expressed by 2, and its Type would be 8-2, Type NL, a Leap year, which is contrary to fact.

Exception (d) applies to the New Moon of Tishri of *a year following a Leap year* occurring on Monday at 32 minutes and 13 parts after 9 A.M. or later. Its NYD must be shifted to Tuesday. The reason for this exception will readily appear from the New Moon computation and Type determination on the facts stated in the exception.

	D	H	M	P	NYD	Ex-press	NYD Diff	Type
Tishri given year	1	09	32	13	TUE	2		
Minus Leap year	5	21	32	13				
Tishri, Leap year	2	12	00	00	THU	4	5	DL

The New Moon of Tishri of the preceding year, computed by substracting the Leap year expression from that of the given New Moon, occurs on Tuesday at noon. Its NYD must be shifted to Thursday, expressed by 4. Its Type is 9-4, Type DL for a Leap year. Without the shifting prescribed by exception (d), the NYD of the given year would be MON, expressed by 1, and the Type of its preceding year would be 8-4, Type N, an Ordinary year, which is contrary to fact.

11

Correlated Type

EVERY one of the six different Types of the Jewish year may have as its corresponding General year one of two different Types: 1) the Ordinary year—OY, or 2) the Leap year—LY. The Type of the Jewish year combined with the Type of its corresponding General year is the Correlated Type. The six Jewish Type variations and the two general Type variations are combined into twelve different Correlated Types as follows:

Ordinary year		Leap year	
D–OY	D–LY	DL–OY	DL–LY
N–OY	N–LY	NL–OY	NL–LY
F–OY	F–LY	FL–OY	FL–LY

Type of the Corresponding General Year

The Jewish year begins in September or October of one General year and ends in September or October of the following General year. The corresponding General year therefore consists of two parts of two consecutive General years. One is the last part of the General year in which Tishri 1 occurs. It runs from September or October to December 31. The second part begins on January 1 and runs to the end of the Jewish year. The General Type variation occurs in February, which is in the second part of the corresponding General year. Therefore, it is the Type of this part of the General year that is shown in the Correlated Type.

Every Jewish year having LY as part of its Correlated Type is, like the General Leap year, divisible by 4. Hence, it may be stated that every Jewish year divisible by 4, except the years 460, 560, 660, 860 and 960, has LY as part of its Correlated Type. The years 460, 560, etc. are those corresponding the General century years of which the hundreds are not divisible by 4.

The Type-Determination-Illustration may now be completed to show the Correlated Type of each year in the series beginning with 714. The years divisible by 4, are 716, 720, and 724. Their Correlated Types have LY. All others have OY.

Type Determinations—Illustration

Year	NYD	Num. Express	NYD Diff	Type
714*	THU	4	5	DL—OY
715	TUE	2	4	N—OY
716	SAT	6	5	F—LY
717*	THU	4	0	FL—OY
718	THU	4	4	N—OY
719*	MON	1	5	DL—OY
720	SAT	6	5	F—LY
721	THU	4	4	N—OY
722*	MON	1	5	DL—OY
723	SAT	6	5	F—OY
724	THU	4	4	N—LY
725*	MON	1	0	FL—OY
726	MON	1		

* Leap years.

12

The General Date Corresponding to Tishri 1, Its GD.

THE GD IS SHOWN BY ONE NUMBER

THE General date correspond-
ing to Tishri 1 is the GD of the Jewish year. The corresponding General year is found instantly by adding 1239
to the Jewish year. The GD discussion deals with the month
and date, both represented by one number. If the number
is 30 or less, it is the date in September. If it exceeds 30,
then the excess is the date in October.

The Jewish Ordinary year varies from 353 to 355 days
and the Leap year varies from 383 to 385 days. The General
year varies from 365 to 366 days. The Jewish Ordinary year
is therefore 10 to 13 days shorter, and the Jewish Leap year
is 17 to 20 days longer than its corresponding General year,
thus causing Tishri 1 of the following year to occur 10 to
13 days earlier, or 17 to 20 days later, in the General year,
than Tishri 1 of the current year. The difference between
the length of the Jewish year and that of its corresponding
General year is known as the Length Difference. It is found
by substracting the days of the corresponding General year
from those of the Jewish year, as follows:

Type	Computation	Length Diff.	Type	Computation	Length Diff.
D–OY	353–365	−12	DL–OY	383–365	18
N–OY	354–365	−11	NL–OY	384–365	19
F–OY	355–365	−10	FL–OY	385–365	20
D–LY	353–366	−13	DL–LY	383–366	17
N–LY	354–366	−12	NL–LY	384–366	18
F–LY	355–366	−11	FL–LY	385–366	19

The minus Length Difference shows that the Jewish year is shorter than its corresponding General year.

GD DETERMINATION BY THE LENGTH DIFFERENCE METHOD

The GD plus the Length-Difference of every Jewish year equals the GD of the following year. If the GD of a given year, for instance, is 10 (Sep. 10) and its Length Difference is 18, then the GD of the following year is 10 plus 18, 28. If the Length Difference of the following year is −11, then the GD of the subsequent year is 28−11, namely: 17. The addition of a minus Length Difference is effected by substracting it. On the basis of the known GD of the first year of a long series of years, the GD's of all the years can be successively determined. Each year's newly determined GD is used as a basis for determining the following GD. This method is demonstrated by the successive determination of the GD's of all the years of the series beginning with 714 on the basis of the known 714 GD, which is Sep. 10. Each year's Length Difference appears under Length Diff. Each year's GD plus its Length Difference determines the GD of the following year.

GD Determination by the Length-Difference Method—
Illustration

Jewish Year	NYD	Corr. Type	Length Diff.	GD	Complete GD
714*	THU	DL–OY	18	10	SEP 10 1953
715	TUE	N–OY	−11	28	SEP 28 1954
716	SAT	F–LY	−11	17	SEP 17 1955
717*	THU	FL–OY	20	06	SEP 06 1956
718	THU	N–OY	−11	26	SEP 26 1957
719*	MON	DL–OY	18	15	SEP 15 1958
720	SAT	F–LY	−11	33	OCT 03 1959
721	THU	N–OY	−11	22	SEP 22 1960
722*	MON	DL–OY	18	11	SEP 11 1961
723	SAT	F–OY	−10	29	SEP 29 1962
724	THU	N–LY	−12	19	SEP 19 1963
725*	MON	FL–OY	20	07	SEP 07 1964
726	MON	D–OY	−12	27	SEP 27 1965

There is no limit to the length of the series of years of which the GD's may be successively determined by the Length Difference method. It must be observed, however, that, unlike the NYD and the TYPE of the Jewish year, which can be determined on the basis of a New Moon of thousands of years ago without first determining the NYD's and TYPES of all prior years, the GD of a given year cannot be determined by this Method on the basis of a known prior GD, unless the GD's of all the intervening years are successively determined.

GD Determination by the Progposticator Method

The Jewish and the General year are both based on the solar year. Each is adjusted to a very near approximation of the solar year by its Leap-year system. Although no individual Jewish year in any way approximates the solar year, the 19-year cycle is a very near equivalent of 19 solar years and is consequently a very near equivalent of 19 General years. The 7 Leap years and the 12 Ordinary years occur regularly in a certain order of sequence in every cycle alike. Each year, having a fixed place, known by its numerical order, in its cycle, has its counterpart in every other cycle. Tishri 1 of any subsequent counterpart is a whole number of cycles and consequently a whole number of General years apart from Tishri 1 of the given year. The GD of the counterpart must therefore be the same as the GD of the given year. The given year thus predicts the GD's of its counterparts and is therefore known as their Prognosticator.

Deviations Affecting GD's

Counterpart GD's may be affected by the following deviations:

a) The cycle is slightly longer than 19 solar years, as shown by the following computation:

	Weeks	D	H	M	S
Cycle	991	02	16	33	03⅓
19 solar years	991	02	14	26	34
Difference	—	—	02	06	29⅓

This small difference accumulates to 2 days, 29 minutes,

and 14⅔ seconds in 23 cycles or 437 years. The GD of a counterpart, 23 cycles subsequent to its Prognosticator, will therefore be two days later than that of its Prognosticator. This difference varies with the length of the separation period.

b) The NYD determination by the application of Rule I frequently requires the shifting of the NYD one or two days from the New Moon of Tishri. Either the NYD of the Prognosticator or that of its counterpart may or may not be shifted. If neither is shifted or if both are shifted equally, the counterpart GD is not affected. If either alone is shifted or if both are shifted unequally, the counterpart GD will be affected by the difference.

c) The General Ordinary year is 5 hours, 48 minutes, and 46 seconds shorter than the solar year. These annual differences are adjusted every fourth year by the addition of one day. If the Prognosticator is at the beginning of such 4-year period and its counterpart is at the end of the third year, when the three annual differences have accumulated to almost a day, the counterpart GD will be one day later, and vice versa.

Deviation (a) may increase considerably over a long period. The period covered by this study is not long enough to show a substantial accumulation. Deviations (b) and (c) may offset each other entirely or partially. The resultant effect over a moderately long period is that the counterpart GD is one to four days later than that of its Prognosticator. However, without attempting to calculate the exact effect of all the deviations, the counterpart GD can be accurately determined on the basis of its NYD.

Exact Counterpart GD Fixed By Its NYD

The counterpart GD must occur on its previously determined NYD. Let us assume that the counterpart GD is the same as that of the Prognosticator, and then find its day of the week in the counterpart year. If it is the day fixed by its NYD, then the assumption is correct. If, however, its NYD is one to four days later, or one to two days earlier, in the week, then its correct GD is respectively just as many days later or earlier than that of its Prognosticator. If the Prognosticator GD, for instance, is SEP. 10, and the day of Sep. 10 in the counterpart year, found in the Perpetual General Calendar, is Thursday, but the Counterpart NYD is Saturday, two days later in the week, then the correct counterpart GD is Sep. 12, two days later than that of its Prognosticator.

The Prognosticator method enables us to determine the GD of a counterpart on the basis of the known GD of its Prognosticator, without first determining the GD's of all the years between the Prognosticator and its counterpart, even if the counterpart is several hundred years subsequent to its Prognosticator.

The years (5)473, 478, and 488, the 1st, 6th and 16th year, respectively, of the 289th cycle, the first cycle within the scope of this study, with known GD's, are used in the following illustrations as Prognosticators in determining the GD's of their counterparts in subsequeunt cycles. The NYD's of the counterparts are determined on the basis of the First New Moon. The day of the Prognosticator GD in the counterpart year is shown next to its NYD. The correct counterpart GD is just as many days later than that of the Prognosticator as its NYD is later than the day of the Prognosticator GD. The correct GD of each counterpart is shown under GD and the complete GD is shown next to it.

GD Determination by Prognosticator Method—Illustrations

Illustration 1, Prognosticator (5)473

	D	H	M	P	NYD	Oct 1 Day	GD	Complete GD
Prognosticator	5	13	51	06	Sat		31	Oct 1 1712
First New Moon	0	23	11	06				
300 cycles	1	21	16	12				
Tishri 701	2	20	28	00	Thu	Tue	33	Oct 3 1940
1 cycle	2	16	33	01				
Tishri 720	5	13	01	01	Sat	Thu	33	Oct 3 1959
1 cycle	2	16	33	01				
Tishri 739	1	05	34	02	Mon	Sun	32	Oct 2 1978
1 cycle	2	16	33	01				
Tishri 758	3	22	07	03	Thu	Wed	32	Oct 2 1997
1 cycle	2	16	33	01				
Tishri 777	6	14	40	04	Mon	Sat	33	Oct 3 2016
10 cycles	5	21	30	10				
Tishri 967	5	12	10	14	Sat	Wed	34	Oct 4 2206
10 cycles	5	21	30	10				
Tishri (6)157	4	09	41	06	Thu	Tue	33	Oct 3 2396

Illustration 2, Prognosticator (5)478

	D	H	M	P	NYD	Sep 6 Day	GD	Complete GD
Prognosticator	0	22	38	13	Mon		6	Sep 6 1717
First New Moon	0	23	11	06				
300 cycles	1	21	16	12				
4 Ord. years	3	11	14	12				
1 Leap year	5	21	32	13				
Tishri 706	5	05	15	07	Sat	Thu	8	Sep 8 1945
1 cycle	2	16	33	01				
Tishri 725	0	21	48	08	Mon	Sun	7	Sep 7 1964
1 cycle	2	16	33	01				
Tishri 744	3	14	21	09	Thu	Tue	8	Sep 8 1983
1 cycle	2	16	33	01				
Tishri 763	6	06	54	10	Sat	Fri	7	Sep 7 2002
1 cycle	2	16	33	01				
Tishri 782	1	23	27	11	Tue	Mon	7	Sep 7 2021
10 cycles	5	21	30	10				
Tishri 972	0	20	58	03	Mon	Fri	9	Sep 9 2211
10 cycles	5	21	30	10				
Tishri (6)162	6	18	28	13	Mon	Thu	10	Sep 10 2401

Illustration 3, Prognosticator (5)488

	D	H	M	P	NYD	Sep 16 Day	GD	Complete GD
Prognosticator	1	17	41	11	Tue		16	Sep 16 1727
First New Moon	0	23	11	06				
300 cycles	1	21	16	12				
10 Ord. years	1	16	06	12				
5 Leap years	1	11	43	11				
Tishri 716	6	00	18	05	Sat	Fri	17	Sep 17 1955
1 cycle	2	16	33	01				
Tishri 735	1	16	51	06	Tue	Mon	17	Sep 17 1974
1 cycle	2	16	33	01				
Tishri 754	4	09	24	07	Thu	Thu	16	Sep 16 1993
1 cycle	2	16	33	01				
Tishri 773	0	01	57	08	Mon	Sun	17	Sep 17 2012
1 cycle	2	16	33	01				
Tishri 792	2	18	30	09	Thu	Tue	18	Sep 18 2031

All the years of the 289th cycle are within the scope of this study. Their GD's are known. The years of many subsequent cycles are within the scope of this study. Their GD's are known. Just as the 1st, 6th, and 16th years of the 289th cycle were used in the foregoing illustrations as Prognosticators to determine the GD's of their respective counterparts, any year of any cycle can be used as Prognosticator to determine the GD's of its counterparts, if the GD of the Prognosticator is known. To determine the GD of any given year by the Prognosticator Method, find the numerical order of the given year in its cycle and then use the corresponding year, with its known GD, of any prior cycle, as Prognosticator.

13

The Three Characteristics of the Jewish Year

THE three elements needed for the preparation of the Jewish annual calendar, namely: its NYD, its CORRELATED TYPE, and its GD, analyzed in the preceding pages, are the Three Characteristics which identify and determine every Jewish year.

TABLE 1. THE THREE CHARACTERISTICS OF THE YEARS 5460 TO 5960

The Three Characteristics of every Jewish year from 460 to 960 (thousands omitted) determined by the methods described and demonstrated in this Section, are given in Table 1. The first two digits of the Jewish year, from 46 to 96, appear in the extreme left column. The last digits, from 0 to 9, are spread across at the head of the Table over 10 triple columns showing the Three Characteristics of every year, namely: its NYD, TYPE, and GD. If the GD is 30 or less, it is the date in September. If its exceeds 30, then the excess is the date in October. The corresponding General year is always the Jewish year plus 1239. The Three Characteristics of any given Jewish year are found as follows.

a) Locate the last digit at the head of the Table.

b) Go down the triple column to meet the line coming across from the first two digits of the given year, where you find the Three Characteristics.

ILLUSTRATION

The Three Characteristics of the year 712 are found in the triple column under 2, where it meets the line coming across from 71. They are MON F—LY 31, signifying that its NYD is Monday, its Type is F—LY and its GD is Oct 1, 1951.

Table 1 and a brief description showing its Composition, Use, and Illustrations are given in PART TWO, as part of the 500-year Correlated Jewish-General Calendar.

IV.

Correlation of the Jewish and General Calendars

14

Correlation Factors

THE wide differences in the basic principles and the individual characteristics of each calendar system have been pointed out time and again throughout this work. Seemingly divergent, the two systems are nevertheless correlated so that the time units of one system are readily convertible into those of the other system. The close reciprocal relationship between the two systems is maintained by the following factors:

1. The fixed numerical relationship between the Jewish year and its corresponding General year.

2. The 19-year cycle is a very near equivalent of 19 General years.

3. The GD is one of the Three Characteristics of every Jewish year.

4. The device used to determine corresponding dates.

CORRESPONDING YEAR DETERMINATION

The fixed numerical relationship between the Jewish year and its corresponding General year enables us to find the General year corresponding to a given Jewish year and the Jewish year corresponding to a given General year. It must be remembered, however, that the 1239 numerical difference between the General year and the Jewish year, in September or October, at the beginning of the Jewish year, is increased to 1240 on the following January 1, when the General year is advanced one year, and is again reduced to 1239 on the following September or October, when the Jewish year is also advanced one year.

THE GENERAL YEAR CORRESPONDING TO A GIVEN JEWISH YEAR

From September or October, at the beginning of the Jewish year, to December 31, the corresponding General year is found by adding 1239 to the given Jewish year. From January 1 to September or October, at the end of the Jewish year, the corresponding year is found by adding 1240 to the given Jewish year.

THE JEWISH YEAR CORRESPONDING TO A GIVEN GENERAL YEAR

From January 1 to the end of the Jewish year (September or October), the corresponding Jewish year is found by subtracting 1240 from the given General year. From the beginning of the new Jewish year (September or October) to December 31, the corresponding Jewish year is found by substracting 1239 from the given General year. If the given General date is in September or October, it may not readily appear whether the corresponding Jewish year is the one coming to an end or the one just begun. Proceed as follows. Assume it to be the year just begun; deduct 1239 and find the GD of the resultant Jewish year in Table 1. If the given General date is later than such GD, then the Jewish year was found correctly. If the given General date is earlier than such GD, deduct 1240 to find the corresponding Jewish year.

The 19-Year Cycle is
a Very Near Equivalent of 19 General Years

The substantial differences between each individual Jewish year and its corresponding General year are reconciled by the Jewish Leap-Year system, so that every 19-year cycle is a very near equivalent of 19 General years. The two calendar systems are thus kept "in step". Furthermore, the Jewish ordinary years and its leap years occur regularly in the same order of sequence in every cycle alike. A given Jewish year, having a fixed numerical place in its cycle, has its counterparts in the same place in every subsequent cycle and is separated from its counterparts by a whole number of cycles, equivalents of 19-General-year periods. The relationship of every counterpart to its corresponding General year must therefore be the same as that of the given year to its corresponding General year. This similarity is the basis of the Prognosticator Method used to determine the GD of a distant counterpart.

The GD Is One of the Three Characteristics
of Every Jewish Year

The GD, as one of the Three Characteristics of every Jewish year, forms the annual tie between the Jewish year and its corresponding General year. The common point fixed at the beginning of the Jewish year serves as a basis for determining corresponding dates throughout the year.

THE DEVICE USED TO DETERMINE CORRESPONDING DATES

The reciprocal relationship between the Jewish and the General corresponding dates is affected by the following variations:

1. The 12 different Correlated Types.

2. The 34 GD variations from September 3 to October 6.

The combined effect is reflected in 12 x 34, 408 possible variations in corresponding dates. 408 different annual calendars would be required to provide for all possible variations. The device described in the following Chapter was adopted to show corresponding dates without the multiplicity of calendars. It is therefore an important link in the Correlation chain.

V.

Calendar Composition

15

Design

In addition to the ordinary calendar functions, the Correlated Jewish-General calendar must provide for finding the General date corresponding to any given Jewish date and the Jewish date corresponding to any given General date. Its varied functions and uses are served by the following specially designed Tables.

Table 1 gives the Three Characteristics of every Jewish year from 5460 to 5960 to be used as a basis for compiling its annual calendar.

Table 2A provides for finding the General date corresponding to any given Jewish date.

Table 2B provides for finding the Jewish date corresponding to any given General date.

Table 3 provides for finding the day of any given Jewish date.

Device Avoiding Multiplicity of Calendars

The multiplicity of calendars, providing for finding corresponding dates for the 34 GD variations of the Jewish year, is avoided by the adoption of the device described in the following chapter.

16

August 31 Assumption

THE Tables 2A and 2B are both based on the assumption that every Jewish year begins on August 31, which is earlier than the actual General date of any given Tishri 1 by a number of days equal to its GD. The General dates shown in Table 2A are therefore earlier, and the Jewish dates shown in Table 2B are therefore later, than their respective actual dates by a number of days equal to the GD of the given or corresponding Jewish year. Consequently, the General dates shown in 2A must be adjusted by adding, and the Jewish dates shown in 2B must be adjusted by subtracting, the GD of the given or corresponding Jewish year. The need for different calendars providing for the 34 GD variations is completely eliminated by the August 31 assumption and is replaced with a simple adjustment for each year. consisting of the addition or subtraction of its GD. The very measure of each year's variation is thus used as the adjustment figure, removing any possibility of error. As one of the Three Characteristics of every Jewish year, the GD is always readily available. In addition to showing the General date of Tishri 1, it is used as the adjustment figure to find corresponding dates.

Before proceeding further with the discussion of Tables 2A and 2B, we now pause to clarify the meaning of certain expressions and to state the rules applicable to additions and subtractions of dates.

MEANINGS OF CERTAIN EXPRESSIONS USED HERE

1. Adding or subtracting a given date or the GD of a given year means adding or subtracting the number of days indicated by the given date or the GD. If the given date, for instance, is June 25 or Tishri 9, the number 25 or 9 is added or subtracted. If the GD of the given year is 10 or 33 (Sep. 10 or Oct. 3), the number 10 or 33 is added or subtracted.

2. The General date of a given Jewish date means the General date corresponding to a given Jewish date. For instance, "the General date of Tishri 1 is September 10" means that September 10 is the General date corresponding to Tishri 1.

3. The Jewish date of a given General date, means the Jewish date corresponding to a given General date. "The Jewish date of July 4 is Tamuz 10" means that Tamuz 10 is the Jewish date corresponding to July 4.

RULES APPLICABLE TO ADDITIONS OR SUBTRACTIONS OF DAYS TO OR FROM A GIVEN DATE

1. If the addition of a number of days to a given date results in a sum exceeding all the days of the month, the excess is the date in the following month. If the sum exceeds the days of the given and the following months, the excess is the date in the subsequent month.

2. If the number of days to be subtracted from a given date exceeds the days of the given date, first add the days of its preceding month to the given date and then substract. The remainder is then the date in the preceding month. If it exceeds the days of the given date plus the days of its preceding month, add also the days of the month prior to the preceding month and then subtract. The remainder is then the date in the month prior to the preceding month.

BASIC DATES

The General date of any given Pewish date equals the General date of the last day of its preceding month plus the given date. If the General date of Tishri 30, for instance, is Oct. 10, then the General dates of Heshwan 1, 9, or 20 are Oct. 11, 19, 30, respectively. Each General date is found by adding 1, 9, or 20 to Oct. 10. The General date of the last day of the preceding month (Oct. 10) is thus used as a basis for determining the General date of any date of the given month. It is therefore designated as the Basic General date of the given month.

Likewise, the Jewish date of any given General date equals the Jewish date of the last day of its pereceding month plus the given date. If the Jewish date of Oct. 31, for instance, is Tishri 10, then the Jewish dates of Nov. 1, 10, 18, or 25 are: Tishri 11, 20, 28, or Heshwan 5, respectively. Each corresponding Jewish date is found by adding 1, 10, 18, or 25 to Tishri 10. The Jewish date of the last day of the preceding month is thus used as a basis for determining the Jewish date of any date of the given month. It is therefore designated as the Basic Jewish date of the given month.

Basic Dates Determination

Based on the Assumption, that the General date of Tishri 1 of every Jewish year is August 31, the General date of Elul 29 is August 30. August 30 is therefore the Basic General date of Tishri, and Tishri 1 is the Basic Jewish date of September (at the beginning of the year). The Basic General date of every Jewish month equals the Basic General date plus the days of its preceding month. The Basic General date of Heshwan, for instance, equals Aug. 30 plus 30, namely: Sep. 29. The Basic General date of Kislev (Type D or N) is Sep. 29 plus 29, namely: Oct. 28. For Type F, it is Sep. 29 plus 30, namely: Oct. 29. The Basic General dates of all the Jewish months of the year, for every Correlated Type, are thus successively determined on the basis of the Basic General date of Tishri, fixed by the Assumption as Aug. 30.

Likewise, the Basic Jewish date of every General month equals the Basic Jewish date plus the days of its preceding month. The Basic Jewish date of October, for instance, is Tishri 1 plus 30, namely: Heshwan 1. The Basic Jewish date of November is Heshwan 1 plus 31, namely: Kislev 3, for Type D or N, or Kislev 2 for Type F. The Basic Jewish dates of all the General months, for every Correlated Type, are thus successively determined on the basis of the Basic Jewish date of September, at the beginning of the year, fixed by the Assumption as Tishri 1.

Only Basic Dates Are Shown in Tables 2A and 2B

Only the Basic General date of each Jewish month is shown in Table 2A, and only the Basic Jewish date of each General month is shown in Table 2B. The General date of any Jewish date in a given month is easily found by adding the given date to the Basic General date of the month, as was already shown. The Jewish date of any General date in a given month is easily found by adding the given date to the Basic Jewish date of the month. The Basic General dates of all the Jewish months of the year, for each Correlated Type, are shown in Table 2A, in a single line, one date for each Jewish month. All the Basic General date variations for the 12 Correlated Types appear in 12 lines. The Basic Jewish dates of all the General months, for each Correlated Type, are shown in Table 2B, in a single line, one date for each General month. All the Basic Jewish date variations for the 12 Correlated Types appear in 12 lines. By using only one Basic date for each month, the need for 12 different annual calendars, for the 12 Correlated Type variations, is eliminated and replaced with a simple adjustment—the addition of the given date to every Basic date shown in either Table. This simple adjustment together with the GD adjustment constitute one composite adjustment formulated as follows:

The corresponding General date is found by adding the given date plus the GD of the given year to the Basic General date shown in Table 2A.

The corresponding Jewish date is found by adding the given date minus the GD of the corresponding Jewish year to the Basic Jewish date shown in Table 2B.

Two Septembers and Octobers in Table 2B

The Jewish year begins in September or October of one General year and ends in September or October of the following General year. The Jewish date corresponding to a September or October date may be either in the year just begun or in the year coming to an end. The September or October at the beginning of the year must be used to find corresponding Jewish dates in the year just begun. Those at the end of the year must be used to find corresponding Jewish dates in the year coming to an end. The preliminary step of finding the corresponding Jewish year indicates which September or October should be used. If the Jewish year was correctly found by deducting 1239 from the General year, use the September or October at the beginning of the year. If 1240 was deducted, use those at the end of the year. Extreme care must be exercised to use the Basic dates under the appropriate September or October. Failure to do so is bound to lead to an erroneous corresponding Jewish date.

17

Table 2A. Corresponding General Dates

THE 12 Correlated Types of the Jewish year appear in the extreme left column. All the months of the Jewish year are spread across at the head of the Table over 13 columns of Basic General dates. The General month over the first Basic date is for every date in the column.

USE

The General date corresponding to a given Jewish date is found as follows:

a) Find the Three Characteristics of the given year, in Table 1.

b) Locate the given Jewish month at the head of Table 2A. Go down to meet the line coming across from the Correlated Type of the year, where you find the Basic General date. Add to it the given date plus the GD of the given year.

c) If the General date is between September and

December 31, add 1239 to the Jewish year to find the General year. From January 1, to September, add 1240.

ILLUSTRATION

Find the General date of Iyar 10, 620.

  a) The Three Characteristics of 620, found in Table 1 are *Thu N—LY 29*
  b) The Basic General date, found in Table 2A, under Iyar, for Type N—LY, is Mar. 24. Adding to it 10 plus 29, we get May 2. The General year is 620 plus 1240. Ans. *May 2, 1860.*

18

Table 2B. Corresponding Jewish Dates

The 12 Correlated Types of the year appear in the extreme left column. The General months, beginning with September of one General year and ending with October of the following General year, are spread across at the head of the Table over 14 columns of Basic Jewish dates. The Jewish month over the first basic date is for every date in the column.

Use

The Jewish date corresponding to a given General date is found as follows:

a) Find the corresponding Jewish year. Between Oct. 10 and Dec. 31, deduct 1239 from the given General year. Between Jan. 1 and Sep. 1, deduct 1240. Between Sep. 1 and Oct. 10, first deduct 1239 and find the GD of the resultant year, in Table 1. If the given date is later than this GD, the Jewish year was correctly found. If it is earlier, deduct 1240.

b) Find the Three Characteristics of the Jewish year, in Table 1.

c) Locate the given General month at the head of Table 2B. (If it is September or October and the Jewish year was found by deducting 1239, use the September or October at the beginning of the year. If 1240 was deducted, use the one at the end of the year.) Go down to meet the line coming across from the Correlated Type of the year, where you find the Basic Jewish date. Add to it the given date minus the GD of the Jewish year.

ILLUSTRATION

Find the Jewish date of May 14, 1948.

a) The Jewish year is 1948 minus 1240, namely 708.

b) The Three Characteristics of 708, found in Table 1 are: *Mon FL—LY 15*

c) The Basic Jewish date, found in 2B, under May, for FL—LY, is Iyar 6. Adding to it 14 minus 15, we get *Iyar 5 708.*

Illustrations of September and October Dates

Given Gen. Date	The Three Charcter.			Basic Jew. Date		Add Adj.	Corresp. Jew. Date			Day
SEP 15 1950	TUE	NL—OY	12	TISH	1	15-12	TISH	4	711	Fri
SEP 15 1954	THU	DL—OY	12	ELUL	12	15-10	ELUL	7	714	Wed
OCT 2 1955	SAT	F—LY	17	HESH	1	2-17	TISH	16	716	Sun
OCT 2 1948	MON	FL—LY	15	TISH	12	2-15	ELUL	28	708	Sat
SEP 20 1955	SAT	F—LY	17	TISH	1	20-17	TISH	4	716	Tue
SEP 15 1955	TUE	N—OY	28	TISH	12	15-28	ELUL	28	715	Thu

The General dates of the first two examples are Sep. 15 of different years. The 1239 deduction found the correct Jewish year in the first example. The basic date was found under the September at the beginning of the year. 1240 was deducted in the second example. The Basic date under September at the end of the year was used. The same is true of the October 2 dates. The last two examples are both September dates in the same year. The 1239 deduction found the correct Jewish year in the first example. The Basic Jewish date was then found at the beginning of the year. 1240 was deducted in the last example. The basic date was then found at the end of the year.

Tables 2A and 2B and a brief description, showing the Composition, Use, and Illustrations, are given in PART TWO, as part of the 500-Year Correlated Jewish General Calendar.

VI.

The Jewish Day Calendar

19

Finding the Day of Any Given Jewish Date

THE Jewish Day Calendar, Table 3, has two parts: The Month-Index and The Monthly Calendar.

THE MONTH-INDEX

The first day of every month is its Month Index. It is derived as follows. Expressing the seven days of the week, from Sunday to Saturday by the numbers 1 to 7 respectively, and expressing the Jewish months in days, with the full weeks discarded, we find that the first day of every month equals the first day plus the days of its preceding month. If Tishri 1, for instance, is on Tuesday, expressed by 3, the day of Heshwan 1 is 3 plus 2, Thursday, and the day of Kislev 1 is 5 plus 1 for Types D and N, or 5 plus 2 for Type F, namely Friday or Saturday respectively. The first day of every month of a given year is thus successively derived from the NYD, the day of its Tishri 1, which is one of its Three Characteristics, found in Table 1. The Month indices of all the months of every Type of Jewish year, based on its NYD, have been derived in this manner and are set forth in the part known as the Month-Index in Table 3.

The six Types of the Jewish year appear in the extreme left column. The NYD's for each Type appear in the adjoining column. All the Jewish months are spread across at the head of Table 3 over 13 columns of Month-Indices. The Month-Index of a given month is found in the column under the given month, where it meets the line coming across from the NYD for the Type of the given year. Before proceeding to find the Month-Index, find the NYD and the Type of the given year in Table 1.

The Monthly Calendar

This part has 7 lines of 7 days of the week, each line beginning on a different day, from Sunday to Saturday. The number in front of each line expresses the first day of the line and shows the Month-Index for which the line is used. Each line is used with the dates underneath as a monthly calendar for the month beginning on the first day of the line, expressed by the Month-Index. The day of any given date appears in this line directly above the given date.

Use of the Jewish Calendar

The day of any given Jewish date is found as follows:

a) Find the NYD and Type of the given year in Table 1.

b) Find the Month-Index in Table 3 in the column under the given month where it meets the line coming across from the NYD for the Type of the given year.

c) Use the monthly calendar line indicated by the Month-Index with the dates underneath as a monthly calendar for the given month. The day of the given date appears in this line directly above the date.

ILLUSTRATION

The day of AB 19, 699 is found as follows:

a) The Three Characteristics of 699, found in Table 1, are
   MON D—OY 26

b) The Month-Index, found in Table 3 under AB on the
   MON line for Type D, is 2.

c) The Monthly Calendar 2—line shows that the day above
   19 is Friday.

Table 3 and a brief description of its composition and
use are given in Part TWO, as part of the 500-Year Correlated Calendar.

VII.

A Glance at the Jewish Year 6000

20

Calendar Forecast for the Year 6000

Long after we are gone, the earth will continue to rotate about its axis every day and to revolve in its orbit around the sun every year. The moon will continue its illumination phases, from New Moon, to Waxing Moon, to Full Moon and to Fading Moon, every month. The sun will continue to rise in the east and to set in the west as it has done for millions of years in the past. The Jewish year 6000 and its corresponding General year 2239-40 will arrive to witness the innumerable changes that will have taken place between now and then.

No one can predict the shape, manner, or form of all the changes. If, however, the two Calendar Systems discussed in this study will survive in their present form, their reciprocal relationship at that time may be predicted with certainty. A complete annual calendar may be set up showing the day and the corresponding General date of every Jewish holiday, festival, etc., of the year 6000.

The Three Characteristics of the Jewish Year 6000

The year 6000 is not within the scope of Table 1. Its Three Characteristics must be determined by the methods demonstrated in this study. Its NYD is based on the New Moon of Tishri, which is derived by computation. Its Type is determined by the difference between its NYD and that of the year 6001. Its GD is determined by the Prognosticator Method, based on the Prognosticator (5)468, which, like the year 6000, is the 15th year in its cycle. The GD of 468, found in Table 1, is Sep. 27. All the corresponding General dates throughout the year 6000 are found by using Table 2A. The day of each date is found by using the Jewish Day Calendar. Tables 2A, 2B, and 3 are not limited in scope to the 500 years covered by Table 1. Every one of these Tables may be used far beyond the year 960, provided the Three Characteristics are first determined.

Dividing 6000 by 19, we find that it is the 15th year in the 316th cycle. The period elapsed since the First New Moon consists of 315 cycles, 9 Ordinary years, and 5 Leap years. Its Three Characteristics are found as follows:

	D H M P	NYD	Sep 27 Day GD	Complete GD
Prognosticator 468	1 16 19 16	Tue	27	Sep 27 1707
First New Moon	0 23 11 06			
300 cycles	1 21 16 12			
15 cycles	5 08 15 15			
9 Ord. years	4 07 18 00			
5 Leap years	1 11 43 11			
Tishri 6000	6 23 45 08	Mon Fri	30	Sep 30 2239
1 Ord. year	4 08 48 12			
Tishri 6001	4 08 34 02	Thu		

The NYD's of 6000 and 6001 are based on their respective New Moons of Tishri. The difference between the 6001 NYD, expressed by 4, and the 6000 NYD, expressed by 1, is 3, indicating Type D. 6000 is divisible by 4. The Correlated Type is therefore D–LY. The day of Sep. 27, 2239, found in the Perpetual General Calendar, is Friday. The 6000 NYD is 3 days later than Friday. Its GD is therefore 3 days later than Sep. 27. It is Sep. 30, 2239. The Three Characteristics of the year 6000 are *Mon D–LY 30*. Its annual calendar is set up by using Table 2A and Table 3.

Annual Calendar of the Jewish Year 6000 — 2239-40

Jewish Date 6000			Gen. Date 2239		Day
Tish	1	Rosh Hashana 1st day	Sep	30	Mon
	10	Yom Kippur	Oct	9	Wed
	15	Succoth 1st day		14	Mon
	21	Hoshana Rabba		20	Sun
	22	Shemini Atzereth		21	Mon
	23	Simchath Torah		22	Tue
Hesh	1	Rosh Chodesh		30	Wed
	21	Weitzman Memorial Day	Nov	19	Tue
Kis	1	Rosh Chodesh		28	Thu
	18	Weitzman's Birthday	Dec	15	Sun
	25	Hanukah 1st day		22	Sun
Teb	1	Rosh Chodesh		27	Fri
			2240		
	6	General New Year's Day	Jan	1	Wed
Sheb	1	Rosh Chodesh		25	Sat
	15	Hamesh Assar	Feb	8	Sat
	16	Weitzman elected President		9	Sun
Adar	1	Rosh Chodesh		13	Mon
	13	Fast of Esther	Mar	7	Sat
	14	Purim		8	Sun
Nis	1	Rosh Chodesh		24	Tue
	15	Passover 1st day	Apr	7	Tue
	21	Passover 7th day		13	Mon
	22	Passover 8th day		14	Tue
Iyar	1	Rosh Chodesh		23	Thu
	5	Israel's Independence Day		27	Mon
	10	Dr. Herzl's Birthday	May	2	Sat
Siv	1	Rosh Chodesh		22	Fri
	6	Shavuot 1st day		27	Wed
Tam	1	Rosh Chodesh	Jun	21	Sun
	17	Fast of Tam 17	Jul	7	Tue
	20	Dr. Herzl's Memorial Day		10	Fri
Ab	1	Rosh Chodesh		20	Mon
	9	Fast of Ab 9		28	Tue
Elul	1	Rosh Chodesh	Aug	19	Wed
	29	Last day of the year 6000	Sep	16	Wed

Part Two

500-Year Correlated
Jewish-General Calendar
5460—5960   1700—2200

VIII.

Guide to Calendar Use

THIS Guide contains all the definitions and instructions that are needed to use this Calendar independently of and apart from the General Study—PART ONE.

21

Definitions

General Calendar is the Gregorian Calendar used in the United States and in many other countries.

"General," used with date, month, or year, denotes the time units of the General Calendar.

"Jewish," used with date, month, or year, denotes the time units of the Jewish Calendar.

NYD is New Year's Day. The General NYD is the day of January 1. The Jewish NYD is the day of Tishri 1.

Type of the General Year. The General year is one of two Types:
OY is the Ordinary year—365 days.
LY is the Leap year—366 days.

General Leap Year. Every General year divisible by 4, except century years of which the hundreds are not divisible by 4, is a Leap year.

General Months and Respective Days

January	31	April	30	July	31	October	31
February	28*	May	31	August	31	November	30
March	31	June	30	September	30	December	31

* February has 29 days in a Leap year.

TYPE OF THE JEWISH YEAR

The Jewish year is one of six Types:

Type	Ordinary Year	Days	Type	Leap Year	Days
D	Deficient	353	DL	Deficient-Leap	383
N	Normal	354	NL	Normal-Leap	384
F	Full	385	FL	Full-Leap	385

Jewish Ordinary Year has 12 months.
Jewish Leap Year has 13 months.
Seven Leap Years in Every 19-Year Cycle. The 3rd, 6th, 8th, 11th, 14th, 17th, and 19th year of every cycle is a Leap year.

FINDING JEWISH LEAP YEAR

Divide the Jewish year (thousands included) by 19. The quotient shows the cycles that have elapsed. The remainder shows which year it is in the current cycle. If it is one of those fixed as Leap years, it is a Leap year. The year 5707, for instance, divided by 19, shows that it is the 7th year in the 301st cycle and it is not a Leap year.

JEWISH MONTHS AND RESPECTIVE DAYS

Month	D	N	F	DL	NL	FL
Tishri	30	30	30	30	30	30
Heshwan	29	29	30	29	29	30
Kislev	29	30	30	29	30	30
Tebet	29	29	29	29	29	29
Shebat	30	30	30	30	30	30
Adar	29	29	29	30	30	30
V-Adar	—	—	—	29	29	29
Nissan	30	30	30	30	30	30
Iyar	29	29	29	29	29	29
Sivan	30	30	30	30	30	30
Tamuz	29	29	29	29	29	29
Ab	30	30	30	30	30	30
Elul	29	29	29	29	29	29
	353	354	355	383	284	385

Correlated Type is the Type of the Jewish Year combined with the Type of its corresponding General year. There are 12 Correlated Types:

D–OY   N–OY   F–OY   DL–OY   NL–OY   FL–OY

D–LY   N–LY   F–LY   DL–LY   NL–LY   FL–LY

THE THREE CHARACTERISTICS

Every Jewish year is identified by its Three Characteristics:

1. Its NYD, the day of Tishri 1.
2. Its CORRELATED TYPE, one of twelve.

3. Its GD, the General date of its Tishri 1.

The General Date of a Given Jewish Date is the General date corresponding to the given Jewish date.

The Jewish Date of a Given General Date is the Jewish date corresponding to a given General date.

Basic General Dates are the General dates given under the Jewish months in Table 2A, used to find corresponding General dates.

Basic Jewish Dates are the Jewish dates given under the General months in Table 2B, used to find corresponding Jewish dates.

Adding or Subtracting a Given Date or the GD of a Given Year means adding or subtracting the number of days indicated by the given date or the GD. If the given date, for instance, is June 25, or Tishri 9, it is the number 25 or 9 that is added or subtracted. If the GD is 10 or 33 (Sep. 10 or Oct. 3), it is the number 10 or 33 that is added or subtracted.

22

INSTRUCTIONS

Tables and Their Use

Table 1 is used to find the Three Characteristics of any given Jewish year from 5460 to 5960.

Table 2A is used to find the General date of any given Jewish date.

Table 2B is used to find the Jewish date of any given General date.

Table 3 is used to find the day of any given Jewish date.

23

Table 1. The Three Characteristics

Composition

The Jewish years 5460 to 5960 are shown here as 460 to 960 (thousands omitted). The first two digits of the year, from 46 to 96, appear in the extreme left column. The last digits, from 0 to 9, are spread across at the head of the Table over 10 triple columns, showing the Three Characteristics of every year from 460 to 960.

Use

The Three Characteristics of a given Jewish year are found as follows:

a) Locate the last digit of the given year at the head of the Table.

b) Go down the triple column to meet the line coming across from the first two digits of the given year, where you find its Three Characteristics.

c) If the GD is 30 or less, it is the date in September. If it exceeds 30, the excess is the date in October.

d) The General year is always the Jewish year plus 1239.

ILLUSTRATION

The Three Characteristics of the year (5)722 are found in the triple column under 2, where it meets the line coming across from 72. They are: *MON DL–OY 11*, indicating that its NYD is Monday, its Type is DL–OY and its GD is SEP 11, 1961.

NOTE

Table I is given on pages 124-127 and again on the back end papers.

Table 1. The Three Characteristics

YR	0 NYD	TYPE	CD	1 NYD	TYPE	GD	2 NYD	TYPE	GD	3 NYD	TYPE	GD	4* NYD	TYPE	GD
46	THU	F–OY	24	TUE	NL–OY	14	MON	F–OY	33	SAT	D–OY	23	TUE	NL–LY	11
47	THU	FL–OY	5	THU	N–OY	25	MON	DL–LY	14	SAT	F–OY	31	THU	N–OY	21
48	THU	FL–LY	14	THU	N–OY	33	MON	F–OY	22	SAT	DL–OY	12	THU	N–LY	30
49	SAT	D–OY	24	TUE	NL–OY	12	MON	F–LY	31	SAT	F–OY	20	THU	DL–OY	10
50	SAT	F–LY	33	THU	N–OY	22	MON	DL–OY	11	SAT	F–OY	29	THU	N–LY	19
51	SAT	DL–OY	13	THU	N–OY	31	MON	F–LY	20	SAT	FL–OY	9	SAT	D–OY	29
52	SAT	F–LY	22	THU	DL–OY	11	TUE	N–OY	29	SAT	F–OY	18	THU	FL–LY	8
53	MON	D–OY	32	THU	N–OY	20	MON	FL–LY	9	MON	DL–OY	28	SAT	D–OY	18
54	SAT	FL–LY	11	SAT	F–OY	30	THU	N–OY	20	MON	DL–OY	9	SAT	F–LY	27
55	MON	D–OY	21	THU	FL–OY	9	THU	N–LY	29	MON	F–OY	17	SAT	DL–OY	7
56	MON	F–OY	30	SAT	D–OY	20	TUE	NL–OY	8	MON	F–OY	27	SAT	F–LY	17
57	MON	DL–OY	11	SAT	F–OY	29	THU	N–LY	19	MON	DL–OY	7	SAT	F–OY	25
58	MON	F–LY	20	SAT	DL–OY	9	THU	N–OY	27	MON	F–OY	16	SAT	DL–LY	6
59	MON	F–OY	28	SAT	F–OY	18	THU	DL–LY	8	TUE	N–OY	25	SAT	FL–OY	14
60	MON	FL–LY	9	MON	D–OY	28	THU	N–OY	16	MON	FL–OY	5	MON	F–LY	25
61	MON	F–OY	17	SAT	FL–OY	7	SAT	D–LY	27	TUE	NL–OY	14	MON	F–OY	33
62	THU	N–LY	29	MON	D–OY	17	THU	FL–OY	5	THU	N–OY	25	MON	DL–LY	14
63	MON	FL–OY	6	MON	F–OY	26	SAT	DL–LY	16	THU	N–OY	33	MON	F–OY	22
64	THU	N–LY	18	MON	DL–OY	6	SAT	F–OY	24	THU	DL–OY	14	TUE	N–LY	32
65	THU	N–OY	26	MON	DL–OY	15	SAT	F–LY	33	THU	N–OY	22	MON	FL–OY	11
66	TUE	NL–OY	5	MON	F–OY	24	SAT	DL–OY	14	THU	FL–OY	32	TUE	N–LY	22
67	THU	DL–OY	16	TUE	N–OY	34	SAT	F–LY	23	THU	FL–OY	12	THU	N–OY	32
68	THU	N–LY	25	MON	FL–OY	13	MON	F–OY	33	SAT	D–OY	23	TUE	NL–LY	11
69**	SAT	D–OY	35	TUE	N–OY	23	SAT	FL–LY	12	SAT	F–OY	31	THU	N–OY	21

* 5 to 9 See pages 125, 127
** 70 to 96 See pages 106, 107

124

Table 1. The Three Characteristics

YR	5 NYD	TYPE	CD	6 NYD	TYPE	GD	7 NYD	TYPE	GD	8 NYD	TYPE	GD	9 NYD	TYPE	GD
46	MON	F–OY	29	SAT	F–OY	19	THU	DL–OY	9	TUE	N–LY	27	SAT	F–OY	15
47	MON	DL–OY	10	SAT	F–LY	28	THU	N–OY	17	MON	FL–OY	6	MON	D–OY	26
48	MON	F–OY	18	SAT	DL–OY	8	THU	F–OY	26	TUE	N–LY	16	SAT	FL–OY	4
49	TUE	N–OY	28	SAT	F–LY	17	THU	FL–OY	6	THU	N–OY	26	MON	DL–OY	15
50	MON	FL–OY	7	MON	D–OY	27	THU	F–OY	15	TUE	NL–LY	5	MON	F–OY	23
51	TUE	N–OY	17	SAT	FL–LY	6	SAT	F–OY	25	THU	DL–OY	15	TUE	N–OY	33
52	THU	N–OY	27	MON	D–OY	16	THU	FL–OY	4	THU	N–LY	24	MON	FL–OY	12
53	TUE	NL–OY	6	MON	F–LY	25	SAT	DL–OY	14	THU	F–OY	32	TUE	N–OY	22
54	THU	N–OY	16	MON	DL–OY	5	SAT	F–OY	23	THU	FL–LY	13	THU	N–OY	32
55	THU	N–OY	25	MON	FL–LY	14	MON	D–OY	33	THU	F–OY	21	TUE	NL–OY	11
56	THU	DL–OY	6	TUE	N–OY	24	SAT	FL–OY	13	SAT	F–LY	33	THU	N–OY	22
57	THU	FL–OY	15	THU	N–LY	35	MON	D–OY	23	THU	FL–OY	11	THU	N–OY	31
58	THU	F–OY	23	TUE	NL–OY	13	MON	F–OY	32	SAT	D–LY	22	TUE	NL–OY	9
59	SAT	F–OY	34	THU	N–LY	24	MON	DL–OY	12	SAT	F–OY	30	THU	N–OY	20
60	SAT	DL–OY	14	THU	N–OY	32	MON	F–OY	21	SAT	DL–LY	11	THU	N–OY	28
61	SAT	F–OY	23	THU	DL–LY	13	TUE	N–OY	30	SAT	F–OY	19	THU	FL–OY	9
62	SAT	F–OY	31	THU	N–OY	21	MON	FL–OY	10	MON	D–LY	30	THU	N–OY	17
63	SAT	DL–OY	12	THU	F–LY	30	TUE	N–OY	19	SAT	FL–OY	8	SAT	F–OY	28
64	SAT	F–OY	20	THU	FL–OY	10	THU	N–OY	30	MON	D–LY	19	THU	FL–OY	6
65	MON	D–OY	31	THU	F–LY	19	TUE	NL–OY	8	MON	F–OY	27	SAT	D–OY	17
66	SAT	FL–OY	10	SAT	F–OY	30	THU	N–OY	20	MON	DL–LY	9	SAT	F–OY	26
67	MON	D–OY	21	THU	FL–LY	9	THU	N–OY	28	MON	F–OY	17	SAT	DL–OY	7
68	MON	F–OY	29	SAT	F–OY	19	THU	DL–OY	9	TUE	N–LY	27	SAT	FL–OY	15
69	MON	DL–OY	10	SAT	F–LY	28	THU	N–OY	17	MON	FL–OY	6	MON	D–OY	26

Table 1. The Three Characteristics

YR	0 NYD	TYPE	CD	1 NYD	TYPE	GD	2 NYD	TYPE	GD	3 NYD	TYPE	GD	4 NYD	TYPE	GD
70	THU	FL-LY	14	THU	N-OY	33	MON	F-OY	22	SAT	DL-OY	12	THU	N-LY	30
71	SAT	D-OY	24	TUE	NL-OY	12	MON	F-LY	31	SAT	F-OY	20	THU	DL-OY	10
72	SAT	F-LY	33	THU	N-OY	22	MON	DL-OY	11	SAT	F-OY	29	THU	N-LY	19
73	SAT	DL-OY	13	THU	N-OY	31	MON	F-LY	20	SAT	DL-OY	9	THU	F-OY	27
74	SAT	F-LY	22	THU	DL-OY	11	TUE	N-OY	29	SAT	F-OY	18	THU	FL-LY	8
75	SAT	F-OY	30	THU	N-OY	20	MON	FL-LY	9	MON	D-OY	28	THU	F-OY	16
76	SAT	FL-LY	11	SAT	D-OY	30	TUE	N-OY	18	SAT	FL-OY	7	SAT	F-LY	27
77	SAT	F-OY	19	THU	FL-OY	9	THU	N-LY	29	MON	D-OY	17	THU	FL-OY	5
78	MON	F-LY	30	SAT	D-OY	19	TUE	NL-OY	7	MON	F-OY	26	SAT	DL-LY	16
79	MON	DL-OY	10	SAT	F-OY	28	THU	N-LY	18	MON	DL-OY	6	SAT	F-OY	24
80	MON	F-LY	19	SAT	DL-OY	8	THU	N-OY	26	MON	FL-OY	15	MON	D-LY	35
81	MON	F-OY	27	SAT	F-OY	17	THU	DL-LY	7	TUE	N-OY	24	SAT	FL-OY	13
82	MON	DL-LY	8	SAT	F-OY	25	THU	FL-OY	15	THU	N-OY	35	MON	D-LY	24
83	MON	F-OY	16	SAT	DL-OY	6	THU	F-LY	24	TUE	NL-OY	13	MON	F-OY	32
84	TUE	N-LY	26	SAT	FL-OY	14	SAT	F-OY	34	THU	N-OY	24	MON	DL-LY	13
85	MON	FL-OY	5	MON	D-OY	25	THU	FL-LY	13	THU	N-OY	32	MON	F-OY	21
86	TUE	NL-OY	15	MON	F-OY	34	SAT	F-OY	24	THU	DL-OY	14	TUE	N-LY	32
87	THU	N-OY	26	MON	DL-OY	15	SAT	F-LY	33	THU	N-OY	22	MON	FL-OY	11
88	THU	N-LY	35	MON	F-OY	23	SAT	DL-OY	13	THU	F-OY	31	TUE	N-LY	21
89	THU	DL-OY	15	TUE	N-OY	33	SAT	F-LY	22	THU	FL-OY	11	THU	N-OY	31
90	THU	N-LY	24	MON	FL-OY	12	MON	D-OY	32	THU	F-OY	20	TUE	NL-LY	10
91	THU	F-OY	32	TUE	N-OY	22	SAT	FL-LY	11	SAT	F-OY	30	THU	N-OY	20
92	THU	FL-LY	13	THU	N-OY	32	MON	D-OY	21	THU	FL-OY	9	THU	N-LY	29
93	THU	F-OY	21	TUE	NL-OY	11	MON	F-LY	30	SAT	D-OY	19	TUE	NL-OY	7
94	SAT	F-LY	32	THU	N-OY	21	MON	DL-OY	10	SAT	F-OY	28	THU	N-LY	18
95	SAT	DL-OY	12	THU	N-OY	30	MON	F-LY	19	SAT	DL-OY	8	THU	N-OY	26

	5			6			7			8			9		
YR	NYD	TYPE	CD	NYD	TYPE	GD	NYD	TYPE	GD	NYD	TYPE	GD	NYD	TYPE	GD
70	MON	F–OY	18	SAT	DL–OY	8	THU	N–OY	26	MON	FL–LY	15	MON	F–OY	34
71	TUE	N–OY	28	SAT	F–LY	17	THU	FL–OY	6	THU	N–OY	26	MON	DL–OY	15
72	MON	FL–OY	7	MON	D–OY	27	THU	FL–OY	15	THU	N–LY	35	MON	F–OY	23
73	TUE	N–OY	17	SAT	FL–LY	6	SAT	D–OY	25	TUE	NL–OY	13	MON	F–OY	32
74	THU	N–OY	27	MON	DL–OY	16	SAT	F–OY	34	THU	N–LY	24	MON	DL–OY	12
75	TUE	NL–OY	6	MON	F–LY	25	SAT	DL–OY	14	THU	N–OY	32	MON	F–OY	21
76	THU	DL–OY	16	TUE	N–OY	34	SAT	F–OY	23	THU	DL–LY	13	TUE	N–OY	30
77	THU	N–OY	25	MON	FL–LY	14	MON	D–OY	33	THU	N–OY	21	MON	FL–OY	10
78	THU	F–OY	33	TUE	N–OY	23	SAT	FL–OY	12	SAT	F–LY	32	THU	N–OY	21
79	THU	FL–OY	14	THU	N–LY	34	MON	D–OY	22	THU	FL–OY	10	THU	N–OY	30
80	THU	F–OY	22	TUE	NL–OY	12	MON	F–OY	31	SAT	D–LY	21	TUE	NL–OY	8
81	SAT	F–OY	33	THU	N–LY	23	MON	DL–OY	11	SAT	F–OY	29	THU	N–OY	19
82	THU	FL–OY	11	THU	N–OY	31	MON	F–OY	20	SAT	DL–LY	10	THU	N–OY	27
83	SAT	D–OY	22	TUE	NL–LY	10	MON	F–OY	28	SAT	F–OY	18	THU	DL–OY	8
84	SAT	F–OY	30	THU	N–OY	20	MON	DL–OY	9	SAT	F–LY	27	THU	N–OY	16
85	SAT	DL–OY	11	THU	N–LY	29	MON	F–OY	17	SAT	FL–OY	7	SAT	D–OY	27
86	SAT	F–OY	20	THU	FL–OY	10	THU	N–OY	30	MON	D–LY	19	THU	FL–OY	6
87	MON	D–OY	31	THU	N–LY	19	MON	FL–OY	7	MON	F–OY	27	SAT	DL–OY	17
88	SAT	FL–OY	9	SAT	F–OY	29	THU	N–OY	19	MON	DL–LY	8	SAT	F–OY	25
89	MON	D–OY	20	THU	FL–LY	8	THU	N–OY	27	MON	DL–OY	16	SAT	F–OY	34
90	MON	F–OY	28	SAT	D–OY	18	TUE	NL–OY	6	MON	F–LY	25	SAT	DL–OY	14
91	MON	DL–OY	9	SAT	F–LY	27	THU	DL–OY	16	TUE	N–OY	34	SAT	F–OY	23
92	MON	F–OY	17	SAT	DL–OY	7	THU	N–OY	25	MON	FL–LY	14	MON	D–OY	33
93	MON	F–OY	26	SAT	FL–LY	16	SAT	D–OY	35	TUE	N–OY	23	SAT	FL–OY	12
94	MON	FL–OY	6	MON	D–OY	26	THU	FL–OY	14	THU	N–LY	34	MON	F–OY	22
95	MON	FL–OY	15	MON	F–LY	35	SAT	D–OY	24	TUE	NL–OY	12	MON	F–OY	31
96	THU	N–OY	27	MON	DL–OY	16	SAT	F–OY	34	THU	N–LY	24	MON	DL–OY	12

24

Table 2A. Corresponding General Dates

The 12 Correlated Types appear in the extreme left column. All the months of the Jewish year are spread across at the head of the Table over 13 columns of Basic General dates. The General month over the first date is for every date in the column.

USE

The General date of a given Jewish date is found as follows:

a) The Three Characteristics of the Jewish year are found in Table 1.

b) Locate the given Jewish month at the head of Table 2A. Go down the column to meet the line coming across from the Correlated Type of the year, where you find the Basic General date. Add to it the given date plus the GD of the year.

c) If the General date is between Sep. and Dec. 31, add 1239 to the Jewish year to find the General year. After Dec. 31, add 1240.

d) If, upon adding a number of days to a given date, the sum exceeds the days of the month, the excess is the date in the following month. If it exceeds the days of the following month too, then this excess is the date in the subsequent month.

ILLUSTRATION

Find the General date of Heshwan 4, 707.

a) The Three Characteristics of 707 (Table 1) are: *THU N—OY 26*.

b) The Basic General date, found in Table 2A, under HESH for Type N—OY, is Sep. 29. Adding to it 4 plus 26, we get Oct 29, 1946.

Table 2A
Genenral Dates Corresponding to Jewish Dates

Table 2A.
General Dates Corresponding to Given Jewish Dates.

	Tish	Hesh	Kis	Teb	Sheb	Adar	V-Ad	Nis	Iyar	Siv	Tam	Ab	Elul
					BASIC	GENERAL	DATES						
Type	Aug	Sep	Oct	Nov	Dec	Jan		Feb	Mar	Apr	May	Jun	Jul
D—OY	30	29	28	26	25	24		22	24	22	22	20	20
D—LY	30	29	28	26	25	24		22	23	21	21	19	19
N—OY	30	29	28	27	26	25		23	25	23	23	21	21
N—LY	30	29	28	27	26	25		23	24	22	22	20	20
F—OY	30	29	29	28	27	26		24	26	24	24	22	22
F—LY	30	29	29	28	27	26		24	25	23	23	21	21
							Feb	Mar	Apr	May	Jun	Jul	Aug
DL—OY	30	29	28	26	25	24	23	24	23	22	21	20	19
DL—LY	30	29	28	26	25	24	23	23	22	21	20	19	18
NL—OY	30	29	28	27	26	25	24	25	24	23	22	21	20
NL—LY	30	29	28	27	26	25	24	24	23	22	21	20	19
FL—OY	30	29	29	28	27	26	25	26	25	24	23	22	21
FL—LY	30	29	29	28	27	26	25	25	24	23	22	21	20

ADJUSTMENT: Add the given date plus the GD of the given year.

Illustrations

Given Date	The Three Character.	Basic Date	Adj. Add	Corresp. Gen. Date	Day
TEB 12 672	SAT F—LY 23	NOV 28	12+23	JAN 2 1912	TUE
HESH 18 675	MON D—OY 21	SEP 29	18+21	NOV 7 1914	SAT
AB 7 675	MON D—OY 21	JUN 20	7+21	JUL 18 1915	SUN
KIS 29 678	MON F—OY 17	OCT 29	29+17	DEC 14 1917	FRI
SIV 21 681	MON FL—OY 13	MAY 24	21+13	JUN 27 1921	MON
KIS 4 684	TUE NL—LY 11	OCT 28	4+11	NOV 12 1923	MON
KIS 17 685	MON F—OY 29	OCT 29	17+29	DEC 14 1924	SUN
TAM 24 688	TUE N—LY 27	MAY 22	24+27	JUL 12 1928	THU
TEB 9 695	MON DL—OY 10	NOV 26	9+10	DEC 15 1934	SAT
HESH 29 698	MON FL—OY 6	SEP 29	29+ 6	NOV 3 1937	WED
TAM 4 698	MON FL—OY 6	JUN 23	4+ 6	JUL 3 1938	SUN
AB 19 699	MON D—OY 26	JUN 20	19+26	AUG 4 1939	FRI
TEB 20 706	SAT DL—OY 8	NOV 26	20+ 8	DEC 24 1945	MON
HESH 4 707	THU N—OY 26	SEP 29	4+26	OCT 29 1946	TUE
ADAR 24 710	SAT D—OY 24	JAN 24	24+24	MAR 13 1950	MON
V-AD 3 711	TUE NL—OY 12	FEB 24	3+12	MAR 11 1951	SUN

25

Table 2B. Corresponding Jewish Dates

COMPOSITION

The 12 Correlated Types appear in the extreme left column. The General months beginning with September of one General year and ending with October of the following year, are spread across at the head of the Table over 14 columns of Basic Jewish dates. The Jewish month over the first date is for every date in the column.

USE

The Jewish date of a given General date is found as follows:

a) Find the Jewish year. If the General date is between Oct. 10 and Dec. 31, deduct 1239 from the General year to find the Jewish year. Between January 1 and September 1, deduct 1240. If it is between September 1 and Oct. 10, deduct 1239 and find the GD of the resultant year, in Table 1. If the given date is later than the GD, it is the Jewish year. If it is earlier, deduct 1240, to get the Jewish year.

b) Find the Three Characteristics of the Jewish year, in Table 1.

c) Locate the given General month* at the head of Table 2B. Go down the Column to meet the line coming from the Correlated Type, where you find the Basic Jewish date. Add to it the given date minus the GD.

d) If a number of days to be deducted from a given date equals or exceeds the given date, first add the days of the preceding month to the given date and then deduct. The remainder is then the date in the preceding month. If it equals or exceeds the given date plus the preceding month, add also the days of the month prior to the preceding month and then deduct. The remainder is then the date in the month prior to the preceding month.

ILLUSTRATION A

Find the Jewish date of April 12, 1954.

a) The Jewish year is 1954 minus 1240, namely 714.

b) The Three Characteristics of 714 (Table 1) are: *THU DL—OY 10.*

c) The basic Jewish date found in Table 2B, under Apr., for the Type DL—OY, is Nis 7. Add to it 12 minus 10, to get Nissan 9, 714.

---

* If the given General date is in September or October and the Jewish year was found by deducting 1239, use the Basic Jewish date under the Sep. or Oct. at the beginning of the year. If 1240 was deducted, use the one at the end of the year.

ILLUSTRATION *B*

Find the Jewish date of SEP. 12, 1902.

a) The Jewish year is found by first deducting 1239 from the General year and finding the GD of the resultant year in Table 1. It is 32. Since the given date is earlier than the GD, deduct 1240 to find the Jewish year. It is 662.

b) The Three Characteristics of 662 (Table 1) are: *SAT DL–OY 14.*

c) The Basic Jewish date, found in Table 2B, under Sep, at the end of the year, for the Type DL–OY, is Elul 12. Adding to it 12 minus 14, we get the Jewish date Elul 10, 662.

Table 2B

Jewish Dates Corresponding to General Dates

Table 2B
Jewish Dates Corresponding to Given General Dates

	Sep	Oct	Nov	Dec	Jan	Feb	Mar	Apr	May	Jun	Jul	Aug	Sep	Oct
					BASIC JEWISH DATES									
Type	Tish	Hesh	Kis	Teb	Sheb	Adar	Nis	Iyar	Slv	Tam	Ab	Elul	Tish	
D—OY	1	1	3	4	6	7	6	7	8	9	10	11	13	
D—LY	1	1	3	4	6	7	7	8	9	10	11	12	14	
N—OY	1	1	3	3	5	6	5	6	7	8	9	10	12	
N—LY	1	1	3	3	5	6	6	7	8	9	10	11	13	
F—OY	1	1	2	2	4	5	4	5	6	7	8	9	11	
F—LY	1	1	2	2	4	5	5	6	7	8	9	10	12	
							V-Ad	Nis	Iyar	Siv	Tam	Ab	Elul	Tish
DL—OY	1	1	3	4	6	7	5	7	7	9	9	11	12	13
DL—LY	1	1	3	4	6	7	6	8	8	10	10	12	13	14
NL—OY	1	1	3	3	5	6	4	6	6	8	8	10	11	12
NL—LY	1	1	3	3	5	6	5	7	7	9	9	11	12	13
FL—OY	1	1	2	2	4	5	3	5	5	7	7	9	10	11
FL—LY	1	1	2	2	4	5	4	6	6	8	8	10	11	12

ADJUSTMENT: Add the given date minus the GD of the Jewish year.

Illustrations

Given Gen. Date	Jewish Year	The Three Character.			Basic Date		Adj. Add	Corresp. Jew. Date			Day
NOV 23 1881	642	SAT F—OY	24		KIS	2	23—24	KIS	1	642	WED
DEC 8 1884	645	SAT F—OY	20		TEB	2	8—20	KIS	20	645	MON
JAN 17 1891	651	MON DL—OY	15		SHEB	6	17—15	SHEB	8	651	SAT
DEC 14 1891	652	SAT F—LY	33		TEB	2	14—33	KIS	13	652	MON
OCT 15 1892	653	THU N—OY	22		HESH	1	15—22	TISH	24	653	SAT
JUL 1 1894	654	MON FL—OY	11		TAM	7	1—11	SIV	27	654	SUN
NOV 2 1896	657	TUE NL—OY	8		KIS	3	2— 8	HESH	26	657	MON
JUN 9 1900	660	TUE NL—OY	5		SIV	8	9— 5	SIV	12	660	SAT
AUG 19 1943	703	SAT DL—OY	12		AB	11	19—12	AB	18	703	THU
NOV 21 1951	712	MON F—LY	31		KIS	2	21—31	HESH	22	712	WED
DEC 26 1952	713	SAT F—OY	20		TEB	2	26—20	TEB	8	713	FRI
APR 12 1954	714	THU DL—OY	10		NIS	7	12—10	NIS	9	714	MON
JUL 26 1956	716	SAT F—LY	17		AB	9	26—17	AB	18	716	THU
MAR 21 1957	717	THU FL—OY	6		V-AD	3	21— 6	V-AD	18	717	THU
MAR 24 1961	721	THU N—OY	22		NIS	5	24—22	NIS	7	721	FRI
SEP 12 1902	662	SAT DL—OY	14		ELUL	12	12—14	ELUL	10	662	FRI

26

Table 3. The Jewish Day Calendar

COMPOSITION

This Table has two parts: 1) the Month-Index and 2) the Monthly Calendar.

MONTH-INDEX

The six Types of the Jewish year appear in the extreme left column. The NYD's for each Type appear in the adjoining column. All the Jewish months are spread across at the head of the Table over thirteen columns showing the Month-Index for every NYD of every Type. It is a number expressing the 1st day of the given month.

MONTHLY CALENDAR

This part has 7 lines of the 7 days of the week; each line begins on a different day, from Sunday to Saturday. The number in front of each line expresses the first day in the line and indicates the Month-Index for which it is used.

USE

The day of any given date is found as follows:

a) The Three Characteristics of the given year are found in Table 1.

b) The Month-Index is found in Table 3, in the column under the given month, where it meets the line of the NYD for the Type of the given year.

c) The Monthly Calendar line indicated by the Month-Index is used with the dates underneath as a monthly calendar. The day of the given date is found in this line above the given date.

ILLUSTRATION

Find the day of Iyar 10, 620.

a) The Three Characteristics of 620 (Table 1) are: *THU N—LY 29.*

b) The Month-Index, found in Table 3, in the column under Iyar, where it meets the line of THU—Type N, is 2.

c) The 2-line of the Monthly Calendar, used with the dates underneath as a monthly calendar shows that the day above 10 is Wednesday.

Table 3
Jewish Day Calendar

Table 3. The Jewish Day Calendar

MONTH-INDEX

TYPE	NYD	TISH	HESH	KIS	TEB	SHEB	ADAR	V-AD	NIS	IYAR	SIV	TAM	AB	ELUL
	MON	2	4	5	6	7	2		3	5	6	1	2	4
D	TUE	3	5	6	7	1	3		4	6	7	2	3	5
	THU	5	7	1	2	3	5		6	1	2	4	5	7
	SAT	7	2	3	4	5	7		1	3	4	6	7	2
N	TUE	3	5	6	1	2	4		5	7	1	3	4	6
	THU	5	7	1	3	4	6		7	2	3.	5	6	1
	MON	2	4	6	1	2	4		5	7	1	3	4	6
F	THU	5	7	2	4	5	7		1	3	4	6	7	2
	SAT	7	2	4	6	7	2		3	5	6	1	2	4
	MON	2	4	5	6	7	2	4	5	7	1	3	4	6
DL	THU	5	7	1	2	3	5	7	1	3	4	6	7	2
	SAT	7	2	3	4	5	7	2	3	5	6	1	2	4
NL	TUE	3	5	6	1	2	4	6	7	2	3	5	6	1
	MON	2	4	6	1	2	4	6	7	2	3	5	6	1
FL	THU	5	7	2	4	5	7	2	3	5	6	1	2	4
	SAT	7	2	4	6	7	2	4	5	7	1	3	4	6

Monthly Calendar

1.	SUN	MON	TUE	WED	THU	FRI	SAT
2.	MON	TUE	WED	THU	FRI	SAT	SUN
3.	TUE	WED	THU	FRI	SAT	SUN	MON
4.	WED	THU	FRI	SAT	SUN	MON	TUE
5.	THU	FRI	SAT	SUN	MON	TUE	WED
6.	FRI	SAT	SUN	MON	TUE	WED	THU
7.	SAT	SUN	MON	TUE	WED	THU	FRI

1	2	3	4	5	6	7
8	9	10	11	12	13	14
15	16	17	18	19	20	21
22	23	24	25	26	27	28
29	30					

27

Short Form Annual Calendars

Use of Tables 2A and 2B to Set Up Annual Calendars

Table 2A can be used to set up an annual calendar of any Jewish year, whose Three Characteristics are known, in the same manner as the annual calendar of the Jewish year 6000 had been set up. Such use is not limited to the 500 years listed in Table 1. The Tables 2A, 2B, and 3 can all be applied to any Jewish year far beyond the year 960, provided its Three Characteristics have first been determined in the same manner as those of the Jewish year 6000 have been determined. Table 2A can thus be used to set up the annual calendar of the current year to be readily available for use throughout the year. An annual calendar can likewise be set up for every Jewish year in advance to show not only Holidays and national events but also birthdays, anniversaries, and other important family events. (The Jewish dates of the Jewish holidays are shown in the calendar of the Jewish year 6000.)

Short Form Annual Calendar

A calendar showing the General date corresponding to

the first day of every month of the Jewish year is a Short Form Annual Calendar, based on Table 2A. The General date corresponding to the first day of the Jewish month is used to derive the General date corresponding to any Jewish date during the month. If, for instance, the General date corresponding to Tishri 1 is Oct. 3, then the General date corresponding to Tishri 10 (9 days later) is Oct. 12, and the General date corresponding to Tishri 15 (14 days later) is Oct. 17. Likewise, a calendar showing the Jewish date corresponding the first day of every month of the General year is a Short Form Annual Calendar, based on Table 2B. The Jewish date corresponding to the first day of the General month is used to derive the Jewish date corresponding to any General date during the month. If, for instance, March 1 is Adar 2, then March 11 is Adar 12, and March 30 is Nissan 2.

Calendar Set-Up

The Short Form Annual Calendar based on Table 2A is set up by adding the date, 1, plus the GD of the year to the Basic General date of every Jewish month for the Type of the given Jewish year. The calendar for the year 720, for instance, is derived by adding 1 plus 33 to the Basic General date of every Jewish Month for the Type F—LY.

Likewise, the Short Form Annual Calendar based on Table 2B is set up by adding the date, 1, minus the GD of the corresponding Jewish year to the Basic Jewish date of every General month for the Type of the corresponding Jewish year. The corresponding Jewish year, however, consists of parts of two different Jewish years with different GD's and of Different Types. One Jewish year ends and the following year begins in September or October. Hence, the GD and Type of the first part are used only for the months of January to September, and the GD and Type of the second part are used for the months of October to December. The addition of 1 minus the GD is actually a subtraction of the difference between the GD and 1. The GD is always more than 1. The calendar of the year 1960, for instance, is derived by adding 1 minus 33 to the Basic Jewish dates of the months of January to September for Type F—LY, and by adding 1 minus 22 to the Basic Jewish dates of the months of October to December for Type N—OY. These are the respective GD's and Types of the Jewish years 720 and 721, parts of the corresponding Jewish year of 1960.

The Short Form Annual Calendars based on Table 2A for the years 720 to 734, and the Short Form Annual Calendars based on Table 2B for the years 1960 to 1974 have been set up in the following pages as illustrations.

Short Form Annual Calendars Based on Table 2A

	720 F–LY	721 N–OY	722 DL–OY	723 F–OY	724 N–LY
	1959	1960	1961	1962	1963
TISH 1	SAT Oct 3	THU Sep 22	MON Sep 11	SAT Sep 29	THU Sep 19
HESH 1	MON Nov 2	SAT Oct 22	WED Oct 11	MON Oct 29	SAT Oct 19
KIS 1	WED Dec 2	SUN Nov 20	WED Nov 9	WED Nov 28	SUN Nov 17
	1960				
TEB 1	FRI Jan 1	TUE Dec 20	FRI Dec 8	FRI Dec 28	TUE Dec 17
		1961	1962	1963	1964
SHEB 1	SAT Jan 30	WED Jan 18	SAT Jan 6	SAT Jan 26	WED Jan 15
ADAR 1	MON Feb 29	FRI Feb 17	MON Feb 5	MON Feb 25	FRI Feb 14
V-AD 1	—	—	WED Mar 7	—	—
NIS 1	TUE Mar 29	SAT Mar 18	THU Apr 5	TUE Mar 26	SAT Mar 14
IYAR 1	THU Apr 28	MON Apr 17	SAT May 5	THU Apr 25	MON Apr 13
SIV 1	FRI May 27	TUE May 16	SUN Jun 3	FRI May 24	TUE May 12
TAM 1	SUN Jun 26	THU Jun 15	TUE Jul 3	SUN Jun 23	THU Jun 11
AB 1	MON Jul 25	FRI Jul 14	WED Aug 1	MON Jul 22	FRI Jul 10
ELUL 1	WED Aug 24	SUN Aug 13	FRI Aug 31	WED Aug 21	SUN Aug 9

Short Form Annual Calendars Based on Table 2A

	725 FL–OY (1964 / 1965)	726 D–OY (1965 / 1966)	727 FL–OY (1966 / 1967)	728 N–LY (1967 / 1968)	729 F–OY (1968 / 1969)
TISH 1	MON Sep 7	MON Sep 27	THU Sep 15	THU Oct 5	MON Sep 23
HESH 1	WED Oct 7	WED Oct 27	SAT Oct 15	SAT Nov 4	WED Oct 23
KIS 1	FRI Nov 6	THU Nov 25	MON Nov 14	SUN Dec 3	FRI Nov 22
TEB 1	SUN Dec 6	FRI Dec 24	WED Dec 14	TUE Jan 2	SUN Dec 22
SHEB 1	MON Jan 4	SAT Jan 22	THU Jan 12	WED Jan 31	MON Jan 20
ADAR 1	WED Feb 3	MON Feb 21	SAT Feb 11	FRI Mar 1	WED Feb 19
V-AD 1	FRI Mar 5	————	MON Mar 13	————	————
NIS 1	SAT Apr 3	TUE Mar 22	TUE Apr 11	SAT Mar 30	THU Mar 20
IYAR 1	MON May 3	THU Apr 21	THU May 11	MON Apr 29	SAT Apr 19
SIV 1	TUE Jun 1	FRI May 20	FRI Jun 9	TUE May 28	SUN May 18
TAM 1	THU Jul 1	SUN Jun 19	SUN Jul 9	THU Jun 27	TUE Jun 17
AB 1	FRI Jul 30	MON Jul 18	MON Aug 7	FRI Jul 26	WED Jul 16
ELUL 1	SUN Aug 29	WED Aug 17	WED Sep 6	SUN Aug 25	FRI Aug 15

149

Short Form Annual Calendars Based on Table 2A

	730 DL–OY	731 N–OY	732 F–OY	733 DL–OY	734 F–OY
	1969	1970	1971	1972	1973
TISH 1	SAT Sep 13	THU Oct 1	MON Sep 20	SAT Sep 9	THU Sep 27
HESH 1	MON Oct 13	SAT Oct 31	WED Oct 20	MON Oct 9	SAT Oct 27
KIS 1	TUE Nov 11	SUN Nov 29	FRI Nov 19	TUE Nov 7	MON Nov 26
TEB 1	WED Dec 10	TUE Dec 29	SUN Dec 19	Wed Dec 6	WED Dec 26
	1970	1971	1972	1973	1974
SHEB 1	THU Jan 8	WED Jan 27	MON Jan 17	THU Jan 4	THU Jan 24
ADAR 1	SAT Feb 7	FRI Feb 26	WED Feb 16	SAT Feb 3	SAT Feb 23
V-AD 1	MON Mar 9			MON Mar 5	
NIS 1	TUE Apr 7	SAT Mar 27	THU Mar 16	TUE Apr 3	SUN Mar 24
IYAR 1	THU May 7	MON Apr 26	SAT Apr 15	THU May 3	TUE Apr 23
SIV 1	FRI Jun 5	TUE May 25	SUN May 14	FRI Jun 1	WED May 22
TAM 1	SUN Jul 5	THU Jun 24	TUE Jun 13	SUN Jul 1	FRI Jun 21
AB 1	MON Aug 3	FRI Jul 23	WED Jul 12	MON Jul 30	SAT Jul 20
ELUL 1	WED Sep 2	SUN Aug 22	FRI Aug 11	WED Aug 29	MON Aug 19

Short Form Annual Calendars Based on Table 2B

		1960		1961		1962		1963		1964	
		720		**721**		**722**		**723**		**724**	
JAN 1		FRI	Teb 1	SUN	Teb 13	MON	Teb 25	TUE	Teb 5	WED	Teb 16
FEB 1		MON	Sheb 3	WED	Sheb 15	THU	Sheb 27	FRI	Sheb 7	SAT	Sheb 18
MAR 1		TUE	Adar 2	WED	Adar 13	THU	Adar 25	FRI	Adar 5	SUN	Adar 17
APR 1		FRI	Nis 4	SAT	Nis 15	SUN	V-Ad 26	MON	Nis 7	WED	Nis 19
MAY 1		SUN	Iyar 4	MON	Iyar 15	TUE	Nis 27	WED	Iyar 7	FRI	Iyar 19
JUN 1		WED	Siv 6	THU	Siv 17	FRI	Iyar 28	SAT	Siv 9	MON	Siv 21
JUL 1		FRI	Tam 6	SAT	Tam 17	SUN	Siv 29	MON	Tam 9	WED	Tam 21
AUG 1		MON	Ab 8	TUE	Ab 19	WED	Ab 1	THU	Ab 11	SAT	Ab 23
SEP 1		THU	Elul 9	FRI	Elul 20	SAT	Elul 2	SUN	Elul 12	TUE	Elul 24
		721		**722**		**723**		**724**		**725**	
OCT 1		SAT	Tish 10	SUN	Tish 21	MON	Tish 3	TUE	Tish 13	THU	Tish 25
NOV 1		TUE	Hesh 11	WED	Hesh 22	THU	Hesh 4	FRI	Hesh 14	SUN	Hesh 26
DEC 1		THU	Kis 12	FRI	Kis 23	SAT	Kis 4	SUN	Kis 15	TUE	Kis 26

Short Form Annual Calendars Based on Table 2B

		1965		1966		1967		1968		1969
JAN 1	FRI	725 Teb 27	SAT	726 Teb 9	SUN	727 Teb 19	MON	728 Kis 30	WED	729 Teb 11
FEB 1	MON	Sheb 29	TUE	Sheb 11	WED	Sheb 21	THU	Sheb 2	SAT	Sheb 13
MAR 1	MON	Adar 27	TUE	Adar 9	WED	Adar 19	FRI	Adar 1	SAT	Adar 11
APR 1	THU	V-Ad 28	FRI	Nis 11	SAT	V-Ad 20	MON	Nis 3	TUE	Nis 13
MAY 1	SAT	Nis 29	SUN	Iyar 11	MON	Nis 21	WED	Iyar 3	THU	Iyar 13
JUN 1	TUE	Siv 1	WED	Siv 13	THU	Iyar 22	SAT	Siv 5	SUN	Siv 15
JUL 1	THU	Tam 1	FRI	Tam 13	SAT	Siv 23	MON	Tam 5	TUE	Tam 15
AUG 1	SUN	Ab 3	MON	Ab 15	TUE	Tam 24	THU	Ab 7	FRI	Ab 17
SEP 1	WED	Elul 4	THU	Elul 16	FRI	Ab 26	SUN	Elul 8	MON	Elul 18
OCT 1	FRI	726 Tish 5	SAT	727 Tish 17	SUN	Elul 26	TUE	729 Tish 9	WED	730 Tish 19
NOV 1	MON	Hesh 6	TUE	Hesh 18	WED	728 Tish 28	FRI	Hesh 10	SAT	Hesh 20
DEC 1	WED	Kis 7	THU	Kis 18	FRI	Hesh 28	SUN	Kis 10	MON	Kis 21

Short Form Annual Calendars Based on Table 2B

		1970		1971		1972		1973		1974	
		730		**731**		**732**		**733**		**734**	
JAN	1	THU	Teb 23	FRI	Teb 4	SAT	Teb 14	MON	Teb 27	TUE	Teb 7
FEB	1	SUN	Sheb 25	MON	Sheb 6	TUE	Sheb 16	THU	Sheb 29	FRI	Sheb 9
MAR	1	SUN	Adar 23	MON	Adar 4	WED	Adar 15	THU	Adar 27	FRI	Adar 7
APR	1	WED	V-Ad 24	THU	Nis 6	SAT	Nis 17	SUN	V-Ad 28	MON	Nis 9
MAY	1	FRI	Nis 25	SAT	Iyar 6	MON	Iyar 17	TUE	Nis 29	WED	Iyar 9
JUN	1	MON	Iyar 26	TUE	Siv 8	THU	Siv 19	FRI	Siv 1	SAT	Siv 11
JUL	1	WED	Siv 27	THU	Tam 8	SAT	Tam 19	SUN	Tam 1	MON	Tam 11
AUG	1	SAT	Tam 28	SUN	Ab 10	TUE	Ab 21	WED	Ab 3	THU	Ab 13
SEP	1	TUE	Ab 30	WED	Elul 11	FRI	Elul 22	SAT	Elul 4	SUN	Elul 14
		731		**732**		**733**		**734**		**735**	
OCT	1	THU	Tish 1	FRI	Tish 12	SUN	Tish 23	MON	Tish 5	TUE	Tish 15
NOV	1	SUN	Hesh 2	MON	Hesh 13	WED	Hesh 24	THU	Hesh 6	FRI	Hesh 16
DEC	1	TUE	Kis 3	WED	Kis 13	FRI	Kis 25	SAT	Kis 6	SUN	Kis 17

Part Three

Perpetual General Calendar

1600 To Infinity

The Perpetual Calendar has two Tables. Table 1 shows the Year-Index of any given year. Table 2 shows the monthly calendar of any given month and the day of any given date.

Table 1 has three parts:

1. The Year-Index, from A to G, is shown in the upper right corner.

2. The year's first two digits, from 16 to infinity appear in the 4 columns under the Year-Index.

3. The year's last two digits, from 00 to 99, appear at the left of the Year-Index.

The Year-Index of any given year is found as follows. Locate the year's last two digits in part 3 and go right across to the Year-Index found directly over the column showing the year's first two digits.

Table 2 has two parts.

1. At the right are 7 lines of the 7 days of the week, from Sunday to Saturday. Each line begins on a different day and is used with the dates underneath as a monthly calendar for the month beginning on the first day of the line.

2. At the left are all the months with all possible Year-Indices under every month.

Having found the Year-Index of the given year in Table 1, locate it under the given month in Table 2 and go right across to the monthly calendar line to be used with the dates underneath as the monthly calendar of the given month. The day of the given date is found in this line directly above the given date.

This calendar can be used for every day, every month and every year from 1600 to Infinity, as follows:

a) Locate the year's last two digits in Table 1 and go right across to its Year-Index above the year's first two digits. The 1918 Year-Index, for instance, is C.

b) Locate this Year-Index under the given month in Table 2 and go right across to the 7-day line to be used with the dates underneath as its monthly calendar. The 7-day line for November, 1918, for instance, is the line beginning with Fri.

c) The day of the given date appears in the 7-day line above the given date. The day of November 11, 1918 (Armistice Day), for instance, is Monday. The Armistice day illustration is shown by the shaded areas in Tables 1 and 2.

d) The date of a certain day of the year, like election day, is found in the monthly calendar under the given day. The 1963 election day, for instance, is found in the November 1963 monthly calendar under the first Tuesday after the first Monday. It is November 5, 1963.

OTHER EXAMPLES

GIVEN DATE	YEAR INDEX	DAY OF GIVEN DATE
Jul 4 1776	C	THURSDAY
Nov 23 1881	G	WEDNESDAY
Dec 8 1884	D	MONDAY
Jan 17 1891	E	SATURDAY
Jan 2 1912	C	TUESDAY
Jun 27 1921	G	MONDAY
Dec 14 1924	D	SUNDAY
Aug 19 1943	F	THURSDAY
Dec 14 2255	B	FRIDAY

PERPETUAL CALENDAR TABLES

TABLE 1 — YEAR INDEX

YEAR'S LAST TWO DIGITS																		YEAR-INDEX			
								00										A	F	D	B
—	06	—	17	23	28	34	—	45	51	56	62	—	73	79	84	90	—	A	F	D	B
01	07	12	18	—	29	35	40	46	—	57	63	68	74	—	85	91	96	B	G	E	C
02	—	13	19	24	30	—	41	47	52	58	—	69	75	80	86	—	97	C	A	F	D
03	08	14	—	25	31	36	42	—	53	59	64	70	—	81	87	92	98	D	B	G	E
—	09	15	20	26	—	37	43	48	54	—	65	71	76	82	—	93	99	E	C	A	F
04	10	—	21	27	32	38	—	49	55	60	66	—	77	83	88	94		F	D	B	G
05	11	16	22	—	33	39	44	50	—	61	67	72	78	—	89	95		G	E	C	A

				YEAR'S FIRST TWO DIGITS
↑	↑	↑	↑	
16	17	18	19	
20	21	22	23	
24	25	26	27	
28	29	30	31	
32	33	34	35	
↓	↓	↓	↓	
and every 4 thereafter to INFINITY				

The red Year-Index **A** or the red digits in Table 1 indicate LEAP YEARS.

For JAN or FEB of **LEAP YEARS** only use the red JAN or FEB in Table 2. All other months are the same for all years.

Shaded areas in Tables illustrate the example: NOV 11, 1918 - MONDAY.

TABLE 2 — THE DAY OF ANY GIVEN DATE

JAN OCT	JAN APR JUL	SEP DEC	JUN	FEB MAR NOV	FEB AUG	MAY		MONTHLY CALENDAR						
A	B	C	D	E	F	G	→	SUN	MON	TUE	WED	THU	FRI	SAT
B	C	D	E	F	G	A	→	MON	TUE	WED	THU	FRI	SAT	SUN
C	D	E	F	G	A	B	→	TUE	WED	THU	FRI	SAT	SUN	MON
D	E	F	G	A	B	C	→	WED	THU	FRI	SAT	SUN	MON	TUE
E	F	G	A	B	C	D	→	THU	FRI	SAT	SUN	MON	TUE	WED
F	G	A	B	C	D	E	→	FRI	SAT	SUN	MON	TUE	WED	THU
G	A	B	C	D	E	F	→	SAT	SUN	MON	TUE	WED	THU	FRI

1	2	3	4	5	6	7
8	9	10	11	12	13	14
15	16	17	18	19	20	21
22	23	24	25	26	27	28
29	30	31				

Number Of Days in Each Month

Jan 31	Apr 30	July 31	Oct 31
Feb 28*	May 31	Aug 31	Nov 30
Mar 31	Jun 30	Sep 30	Dec 31

* 29 days in Leap Years

Index

Table 1. The Three Characteristics

YR		0			1			2			3			4	
	NYD	TYPE	CD	NYD	TYPE	GD	NYD	TYPE	GD	NYD	TYPE	GD	NYD	TYPE	GD
46	THU	F—OY	24	TUE	NL—OY	14	MON	F—OY	33	SAT	D—OY	23	TUE	NL—LY	11
47	THU	FL—OY	5	THU	N—OY	25	MON	DL—LY	14	SAT	F—OY	31	THU	N—OY	21
48	THU	FL—LY	14	THU	N—OY	33	MON	F—OY	22	SAT	DL—OY	12	THU	N—LY	30
49	SAT	D—OY	24	TUE	NL—OY	12	MON	F—LY	31	SAT	F—OY	20	THU	DL—OY	10
50	SAT	F—LY	33	THU	N—OY	22	MON	DL—OY	11	SAT	F—OY	29	THU	N—LY	19
51	SAT	DL—OY	13	THU	N—OY	31	MON	F—LY	20	SAT	FL—OY	9	SAT	D—OY	29
52	SAT	F—LY	22	THU	DL—OY	11	TUE	N—OY	29	SAT	F—OY	18	THU	FL—LY	8
53	MON	D—OY	32	THU	N—OY	20	MON	FL—LY	9	MON	F—OY	28	SAT	D—OY	18
54	SAT	FL—LY	11	SAT	F—OY	30	THU	N—OY	20	MON	DL—OY	9	SAT	F—LY	27
55	MON	D—OY	21	THU	FL—OY	9	THU	N—LY	29	MON	F—OY	17	SAT	DL—OY	7
56	MON	F—OY	30	SAT	D—OY	20	TUE	NL—OY	8	MON	F—OY	27	SAT	F—LY	17
57	MON	DL—OY	11	SAT	F—OY	29	THU	N—LY	19	MON	DL—OY	7	SAT	F—OY	25
58	MON	F—LY	20	SAT	DL—OY	9	THU	N—OY	27	MON	F—OY	16	SAT	DL—LY	6
59	MON	F—OY	28	SAT	F—OY	18	THU	DL—LY	8	TUE	N—OY	25	SAT	FL—OY	14
60	MON	FL—LY	9	MON	D—OY	28	THU	N—OY	16	MON	FL—OY	5	MON	F—LY	25
61	MON	F—OY	17	SAT	FL—OY	7	SAT	D—LY	27	TUE	NL—OY	14	MON	F—OY	33
62	THU	N—LY	29	MON	D—OY	17	THU	FL—OY	5	THU	N—OY	25	MON	DL—LY	14
63	MON	FL—OY	6	MON	F—OY	26	SAT	DL—LY	16	THU	N—OY	33	MON	F—OY	22
64	THU	N—LY	18	MON	DL—OY	6	SAT	F—OY	24	THU	DL—OY	14	TUE	N—LY	32
65	THU	N—OY	26	MON	DL—OY	15	SAT	F—LY	33	THU	N—OY	22	MON	FL—OY	11
66	TUE	NL—OY	5	MON	F—OY	24	SAT	DL—OY	14	THU	F—OY	32	TUE	N—LY	22
67	THU	DL—OY	16	TUE	N—OY	34	SAT	F—LY	23	THU	FL—OY	12	THU	N—OY	32
68	THU	N—LY	25	MON	FL—OY	13	MON	F—OY	33	SAT	D—OY	23	TUE	NL—LY	11
69	SAT	D—OY	35	TUE	N—OY	23	SAT	FL—LY	12	SAT	F—OY	31	THU	N—OY	21
70	THU	FL—LY	14	THU	N—OY	33	MON	F—OY	22	SAT	DL—OY	12	THU	N—LY	30
71	SAT	D—OY	24	TUE	NL—OY	12	MON	F—LY	31	SAT	F—OY	20	THU	DL—OY	10
72	SAT	F—LY	33	THU	N—OY	22	MON	DL—OY	11	SAT	F—OY	29	THU	N—LY	19
73	SAT	DL—OY	13	THU	N—OY	31	MON	F—LY	20	SAT	DL—OY	9	THU	F—OY	27
74	SAT	F—LY	22	THU	DL—OY	11	TUE	N—OY	29	SAT	F—OY	18	THU	FL—LY	8
75	SAT	F—OY	30	THU	N—OY	20	MON	FL—LY	9	MON	D—OY	28	THU	F—OY	16
76	SAT	FL—LY	11	SAT	D—OY	30	TUE	N—OY	18	SAT	FL—OY	7	SAT	F—LY	27
77	SAT	F—OY	19	THU	FL—OY	9	THU	N—LY	29	MON	D—OY	17	THU	FL—OY	5
78	MON	F—LY	30	SAT	D—OY	19	TUE	NL—OY	7	MON	F—OY	26	SAT	DL—LY	16
79	MON	DL—OY	10	SAT	F—OY	28	THU	N—LY	18	MON	DL—OY	6	SAT	F—OY	24
80	MON	F—LY	19	SAT	DL—OY	8	THU	N—OY	26	MON	FL—OY	15	MON	D—LY	35
81	MON	F—OY	27	SAT	F—OY	17	THU	DL—LY	7	TUE	N—OY	24	SAT	FL—OY	13
82	MON	DL—LY	8	SAT	F—OY	25	THU	FL—OY	15	THU	N—OY	35	MON	D—LY	24
83	MON	F—OY	16	SAT	DL—OY	6	THU	F—LY	24	TUE	NL—OY	13	MON	F—OY	32
84	TUE	N—LY	26	SAT	FL—OY	14	SAT	F—OY	34	THU	N—OY	24	MON	DL—LY	13
85	MON	FL—OY	5	MON	D—OY	25	THU	FL—LY	13	THU	N—OY	32	MON	F—OY	21
86	TUE	NL—OY	15	MON	F—OY	34	SAT	F—OY	24	THU	DL—OY	14	TUE	N—LY	32
87	THU	N—OY	26	MON	DL—OY	15	SAT	F—LY	33	THU	N—OY	22	MON	FL—OY	11
88	THU	N—LY	35	MON	F—OY	23	SAT	DL—OY	13	THU	F—OY	31	TUE	N—LY	21
89	THU	DL—OY	15	TUE	N—OY	33	SAT	F—LY	22	THU	FL—OY	11	THU	N—OY	31
90	THU	N—LY	24	MON	FL—OY	12	MON	D—OY	32	THU	F—OY	20	TUE	NL—LY	10
91	THU	F—OY	32	TUE	N—OY	22	SAT	FL—LY	11	SAT	D—OY	30	THU	N—OY	20
92	THU	FL—LY	13	THU	N—OY	32	MON	D—OY	21	THU	FL—OY	9	THU	N—LY	29
93	THU	F—OY	21	TUE	NL—OY	11	MON	F—OY	30	SAT	D—OY	19	TUE	NL—OY	7
94	SAT	F—LY	32	THU	N—OY	21	MON	DL—OY	10	SAT	F—OY	28	THU	N—LY	18
95	SAT	DL—OY	12	THU	N—OY	30	MON	F—LY	19	SAT	DL—OY	8	THU	N—OY	26
96	SAT	F—OY	21	THU	DL—OY	11	TUE	N—OY	29	SAT	F—OY	18	THU	FL—LY	8